Executive Calculator Guidebook

Note: The calculator keystrokes and descriptions used in this book were based on the *Business Analyst-II*™ financial calculator. The facts and information included will be generally useful when working with other specially dedicated business calculators, but the keystroke sequences described will only apply directly to the *Business Analyst-II*™ calculator.

IMPORTANT

Record the serial number from the bottom of the unit and purchase date in the space below. The serial number is identified by the words "SER. NO." on the bottom case. Always reference this information in any correspondence.

BA-II		
Model No.	Serial No.	Purchase Date

This book was developed by:

Elbert B. Greynolds, Jr., Ph.D., CPA,
Associate Professor of Accounting
Edwin L. Cox School of Business
Southern Methodist University

and

The Staff of the Texas Instruments Learning Center:
Jan E. Stevens

With contributions by:
Mahendra P. Agrawal
Jacquelyn F. Quiram
Deanna G. Bell
Lane L. Douglas

Artwork and layout were coordinated and executed by:
Schenck Design Associates, Inc.

ISBN 0-89512-040-2

Library of Congress Catalogue Number: 80-52101

TABLE OF CONTENTS

Table of Contents

Table of Contents

CHAPTER
1 INTRODUCTION

Every profession has its particular "tools of the trade." In business, one of the most important tools you can have is a device that helps you evaluate financial alternatives. That's where the *Business Analyst-II*™ financial calculator can come in handy.

This calculator has been designed especially for you, the business person. Its special functions — financial, profit margin, and statistical — are related specifically to business applications. For example, you may have to decide whether to invest in a savings account or a capital asset. If you choose the savings account, you may then need to select the savings institution which offers you the best interest rate. If you plan to invest in the capital asset, you may have to choose between leasing or buying the product. Although these may seem to be easy decisions at first glance, many complex calculations are involved in selecting the option which will be the most profitable for you or your company.

Time is another important factor in many decisions. By using your calculator to quickly perform the mathematical computations, you can often spend more time considering all of your alternatives. In this way, your calculator can help you become a better informed decision maker where financial matters are involved.

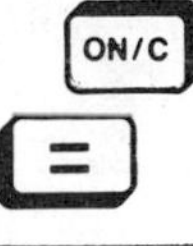

Using This Book

We have designed this book to be exactly what its name suggests —a "guidebook." This means that we've concentrated on including as many real-life examples as possible, rather than emphasizing theory and formulas. Occasionally, however, you'll find a brief explanation included with an example, but only when some of the terminology or the solution procedure in the example needs additional clarification. Also, *Appendix A* lists the formulas used in the profit-margin, financial, and statistical calculations and in the conversion routines and specialized financial models, such as Economic Order Quantity (EOQ). If the formula has been included, the example refers you to the appendix.

The applications in the book represent situations that are encountered often in the business world. Notice that each example includes three columns of information, titled *Procedure*, *Press*, and *Display*. The *Procedure* column gives a generalized description of the method used to solve the problem. The *Press* column illustrates the keystroke sequence, and the *Display* column shows you the results which appear in your calculator's display.

To make specific applications easier to find, we've given each example a task-oriented heading. Therefore, to use this book, just follow this simple procedure:

1. Decide what type of problem you need to solve by considering the information you have and the information you need.
2. Look in the Table of Contents and find the heading which most closely resembles the type of problem you want to solve.
3. After locating an appropriate example, follow the step-by-step keystroke sequence and enter your values instead of ours.

That's all there is to it! Now you're ready to start using your *Business Analyst-II*™ calculator. If you have questions about any of the calculator's functions, the next section describes the use(s) of each key.

CHAPTER
1 A Look at the Keys

To become more familiar with your *Business Analyst-II*™ calculator, read this section completely. It explains the basic features of the calculator, as well as the function of each key. For practice using the keys, work some of the problems in the remaining chapters of the book.

Features

The following features add to the value and convenience of your calculator:

- Easy to read Liquid Crystal Display (LCD).
- *Constant Memory*™ feature holds numbers in mode registers and user memory even when the calculator is turned off.
- *APD*™ Automatic Power Down provides for special power-saving features. The calculator turns itself off completely after typically 5 to 15 minutes of nonuse. You will never waste a set of batteries by forgetting to turn your calculator off or by having it turned on accidentally. This feature can increase the life of each set of batteries up to 50%.
- Battery indicator provides information on battery condition.
- Up to 1000 hours of operation can normally be achieved from a fresh set of batteries.
- Accuracy — The internal calculating capacity is 11 digits even though only 8 digits can be displayed. The 8-digit displayed number is generally rounded to within ± 1 in the 8th digit for all functions except where noted.

Functions

These financial, business, and statistical functions make your calculator a powerful and versatile tool.

- *Mathematical functions include:*
  - Arithmetic (+, −, ×, ÷)
  - Square (x^2) and Square Root ($\sqrt{x}$)
  - Natural Logarithm (lnx) and Antilogarithm (e^x)
  - Universal Powers (y^x)
  - Reciprocal (1/x)
  - Percent (%)
  - Percent Change (Δ%)

- *Profit Margin functions provide for easy calculations involving:*
  - Cost
  - Selling Price
  - Profit Margin
- *Financial capabilities solve problems involving:*
  - Simple Interest
  - Compound Interest
  - Rent Schedules
  - Mortgages
  - Savings Accounts
  - Installment Loans
  - Insurance Plans
  - Annuities
  - Add-On Interest
  - Amortization Schedules
  - Bond Yields
  - Bond Analyses (Discounting)
  - Depreciation
- *Statistical functions include:*
  - Linear Regression routine — immediate statistical analysis of data and projection of new points. Trend-Line Analysis is also available.
  - Mean, Standard Deviation and Correlation — analyze one- or two-dimensional statistical data.

On and Off Keys — [ON/C], [OFF]

[ON/C] — If the calculator is OFF, pressing [ON/C] once turns the calculator on. A "▲" and a " 0 " appear in the display. The first time you turn on the calculator, or after you replace the batteries, clear the calculator completely by pressing [ON/C], [ON/C], [STO], [2nd] [CMR], and [FIX] [8].

The [ON/C] key also functions as a clearing key. Pressing [ON/C] once, before any function or operation key is pressed, clears the last number you entered into the calculator. If [ON/C] is pressed after a function or operation key (including the [=] key), the display, the constant, and any pending calculation are cleared.

The display, the constant, and any pending calculation are always cleared by pressing [ON/C] twice. Pressing this key does not affect the memory and mode registers.

[OFF] — This key turns the calculator off and clears any uncompleted calculation.

CHAPTER

1 A Look at the Keys

NOTE: Pressing and holding down any key on the top row of your calculator will cause random segments to be displayed. These random segments do not affect normal operations of the calculator and will fade away or disappear when the key is released. Also, the entire display, including the small "▲" battery condition indicator, is blanked during key entries and calculations.

Constant Memory™ **Feature**

Even when your calculator is turned off, the Constant Memory feature saves the memory content, the number of decimal places selected, the last constant, the mode, and all values entered in the same mode (profit-margin, financial, or statistical) prior to turning the calculator off. Normal clearing functions are in effect when the calculator is turned back on. For example, pressing [ON/C] twice will clear the constant, pressing [2nd] [Mode] will clear all data entered in the previous mode, or pressing [2nd] [CMR] will clear the mode registers.

IMPORTANT: The Constant Memory feature is not maintained if the batteries are discharged or removed.

Display Indicators

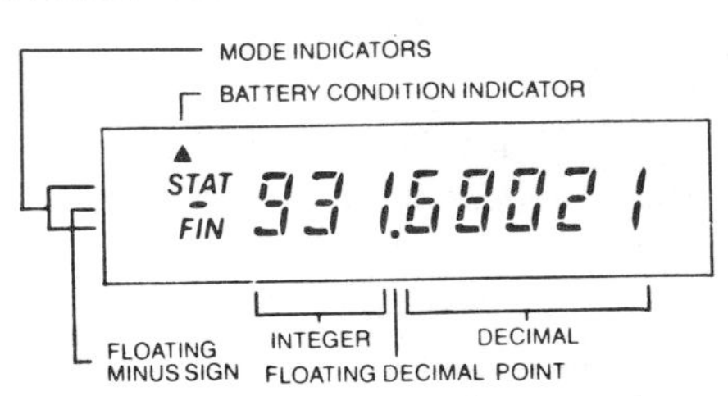

NOTE: Eight digits may be entered into the display. Any digit keys pressed after the eighth are ignored. For numbers with a decimal, a maximum of seven digits may be entered to the right of the decimal point.

Battery Condition Indicator. The small "▲" in the upper left-hand portion of the display indicates a "good battery" condition. When "▲" becomes very dim or disappears, it means that the batteries are becoming weak and should be replaced. However, the batteries may still operate the calculator for several more hours before it begins to operate erratically. See the Service Information Appendix for battery replacement instructions.

Mode Indicators. "STAT" indicates statistical mode. "FIN" indicates financial mode. The absence of both "STAT" and "FIN" indicates profit-margin mode.

Floating Minus Sign. Any negative number is displayed with a minus sign immediately to the left of the number, just as negative numbers are normally written.

***APD*™ Automatic Power Down**

If no keys are pressed for a period of about 5 to 15 minutes, the APD feature will cause your calculator to turn off automatically. When this happens, any pending calculation is lost. Press [ON/C] to turn the calculator on again. (The Constant Memory feature functions in the same way as when [OFF] is pressed.)

To cancel the APD feature, simultaneously press any keys in the second, fourth, and fifth columns (such as [0], [+/−], and [=]). The cancellation remains in effect until the calculator is turned off.

Number Entry Keys — [0] - [9], [•], [+/−], [x:y]

Your calculator operates with a floating decimal point, and numbers are entered into the machine with the entry keys: [0] - [9], [•], [+/−], and [x:y]. As you enter any number, the decimal point is assumed (but not displayed) to the right of your entry until the decimal point key is pressed. After pressing the decimal key [•], the fractional part of the number is keyed in, and the decimal point "floats" to the left with it. To change the sign of a number in the display, just push the change sign key [+/−] once. Pressing [+/−] a second time changes the sign back again. The x exchange y key [x:y] exchanges the displayed number with the content of the y register. This key is used to exchange divisor and dividend in division problems and to enter data and display results in certain financial and statistical calculations.

Fixed Decimal Key — [FIX]

This key sets a fixed number of digits to the right of the decimal point. Press [FIX] and then a number key ([0] through [7]) corresponding to the number of decimal places you want to the right of the decimal point. Press [FIX] [8] or [FIX] [9] anytime you want to return to a floating decimal display.

Using a fixed-decimal display does not affect the accuracy of your calculations. The calculator uses all internal digits (up to 11) for subsequent calculations. For example, if [FIX] [2] has been selected and an actual result is 6.158, the calculator displays the rounded value of 6.16 as the result. However, the calculator internally carries the actual 6.158 value to the subsequent calculation or memory (if used).

Note that your calculator can display unexpected results when you press [FIX] 0 (no digits appear to the right of the decimal point). For example, if you press [FIX] 0 and then calculate 1 [÷] 3 [=], the display shows a result of zero. To display the normal floating-decimal value, press [FIX] 9.

Remember that the fixed-decimal selection is retained by the *Constant Memory*™ feature. A fixed-decimal selection remains in effect until you change it or until the batteries are removed or become discharged.

Extended Display Range (Scientific Notation)

The normal display range of your calculator is between 0.0000001 and 99999999 (positive or negative). If a result is smaller or larger than the normal display range, the calculator automatically switches the display into scientific notation. In scientific notation, the display value splits into two fields, the mantissa and the power-of-ten exponent. For example, the result of the calculation:

−0.0036089 [÷] 10000000 [=]

is expressed as -3.6089×10^{-10} by your calculator. The calculator display shows:

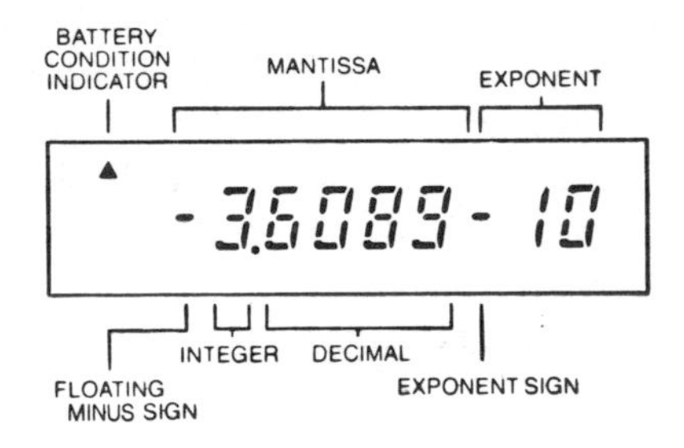

In scientific notation, a positive exponent indicates how many places the decimal point should be shifted to the right. If the exponent is negative, the decimal should be moved to the left. In the last example, move the decimal point 10 places to the left to obtain the result in normal form:

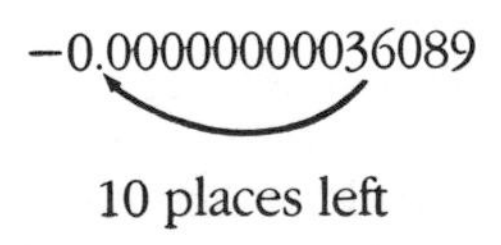

Basic Operation Keys — [+], [−], [×], [÷], [=]

Basic arithmetic is handled with five operation keys: [+], [−], [×], [÷], and [=]. Each time you press an operation key, including [Δ%] and [y^x], the previous operation is completed. All of the basic operation keys can be used in any of the three modes — profit-margin, financial, and statistical.

[+] — The Add Key tells the calculator to add the next number you enter to the number displayed.

[−] — The Subtract Key tells the calculator to subtract the next number you enter from the number displayed.

[×] — The Multiply Key tells the calculator to multiply the displayed number by the next number you enter. The displayed value must be less than 1×10^{99} or an error condition may result.

[÷] — The Divide Key tells the calculator to divide the displayed number by the next number you enter.

[=] — The Equals Key completes all previously entered operations. This key is used to obtain both intermediate and final results.

Entry errors can be corrected easily by pressing the correct arithmetic function, [y^x] or [Δ%] key immediately after the incorrect function, or by using the clear-entry function of the [ON/C] key.

Example: Calculate 6 ~~+~~ × 7 ~~−~~ + ~~4~~ 3 = 45.

Procedure	Press	Display
1. Clear calculator and select floating decimal point.	[ON/C] [FIX] 8	**0**
2. Enter 6 and change + to ×.	6 [+] [×]	**6**
3. Enter 7 and change − to +.	7 [−] [+]	**42**
4. Enter 4.	4	**4**
5. Change 4 to 3.	[ON/C] 3	**3**
6. Calculate result.	[=]	**45**

Second Function Key — [2nd]

Your calculator has many features to make calculations easy and accurate. To allow you access to all of these features, without overloading the keyboard, many of the calculator keys have more than one function.

The first function is printed on the key. To use the first function, just press the key. The second function of a key is printed directly above it. To use a second function, just press the [2nd] key (located on the upper left-hand corner of the keyboard) and then the function key. When [2nd] is pressed twice, the calculator performs the first function operation. If [2nd] is pressed before a digit key, [+/-], or [.], the [2nd] operation is ignored.

In this book, we'll use keys with a black background ■ to indicate second functions. For instance, to use the second function square root of x, press [2nd] [$\sqrt{x}$].

Square, Square Root and Reciprocal Keys — [x^2], [2nd] [$\sqrt{x}$], [1/x]

These three keys come in quite handy for the speedy handling of a variety of algebraic and equation-solving situations. All three keys act immediately on the number in the display (called x), and don't affect the calculations in progress.

[x^2] — The Square Key multiplies the number (x) in the display by itself and displays the result.

[2nd] [$\sqrt{x}$] — The Square Root Key sequence finds the number that when multiplied by itself gives you the displayed number (x) back. (x cannot be negative).

[1/x] — The Reciprocal Key divides the displayed number (x) into one. (x cannot be zero.)

A Look at the Keys

Universal Power Key — 2nd y^x

This key allows you to raise a positive number to a power. To use this key:

- Enter the number (y) you want to raise to a power.
- Press 2nd y^x.
- Enter the power (x).
- Press = (or any basic operation key).

To take the "xth" root of any number y ($\sqrt[x]{y}$):

- Enter the number (y) whose root you want to find.
- Press 2nd y^x.
- Enter the root (x).
- Press 1/x.
- Press = (or any basic operation key).

In either case, the variable y must be a positive number. Also, attempting to take the 0th root of a number results in an error condition.

Example: Find 2^3.

Procedure	Press	Display
1. Enter y.	2 2nd y^x	**2**
2. Enter x.	3	**3**
3. Calculate result.	=	**8**

Logarithm Keys — 2nd lnx, 2nd e^x

2nd lnx — The Natural Logarithm Key displays the natural logarithm (base e) of the number (x) in the display. (x cannot be negative or zero.)

2nd e^x — The Natural Antilogarithm Key (e to the Power x Key) calculates the natural antilogarithm (base e) of the number (x) in the display.

Both of these keys act immediately on the number in the display — and don't affect calculations in progress.

Example: Find the natural logarithm of 1.2 and the natural antilogarithm of 1.25.

Procedure	Press	Display
1. Calculate logarithm of 1.2.	1.2 2nd lnx	**0.1823216**
2. Compute antilogarithm of 1.25.	1.25 2nd e^x	**3.490343**

Percent and Percent Change Keys — [%], [2nd] [Δ%]

These keys are handy for a wide variety of business percentage calculations.

The symbol % means percent, which is "one hundredth." The term 75% can also be written as .75, or 75/100, or even 3/4.

When the [%] key is pressed, the number in the display is immediately converted to a decimal percent (divided by 100). If you enter 43.9 and press [%], 0.439 is displayed.

The real power of the [%] key is turned on for you when you use it in combination with an operation key. These keys sequences allow "mark up," "mark down," and other percentage problems to be solved easily.

[+] n [%] [=] Adds n% to the original number displayed (especially good for sales tax computations).

[−] n [%] [=] Subtracts n% from the original number displayed (very useful when finding the marked down sale price of an item).

[×] n [%] [=] Multiplies the original number in the display by n%.

[÷] n [%] [=] Divides the original number in the display by n%.

[2nd] [Δ%] — The Percent Change (or "Delta Percent") Key calculates the percentage change between two values x_1 and x_2, where:

$$\Delta\,\% = \frac{x_1 - x_2}{x_2} \times 100$$

This kind of calculation comes up frequently in business situations. For example, let's say you keep track of the mileage you get from your car, and for a while you've been getting 17.0 miles per gallon. You have your car tuned up, and the mileage jumps to 19.8 MPG. What's the percentage increase?

Procedure	Press	Display
1. Enter new mileage (x_1).	19.8 [2nd] [Δ%]	**19.8**
2. Enter old mileage (x_2).	17	**17**
3. Calculate percent change.	[=]	**16.470588**

Constant Key — [K]

This key stores a number and an operation (+, −, ×, ÷, Δ % or %) for use in repetitive calculations. Select any of the following key sequences to input a constant value (M) and a constant math operaton. Then you just enter a new number and press [=]. The calculator automatically supplies the math operation and constant value needed to complete the problem.

[+] [K] M [=] — adds M to each subsequent entry.

[−] [K] M [=] — subtracts M from each subsequent entry.

[×] [K] M [=] — multiplies each subsequent entry by M.

[÷] [K] M [=] — divides each subsequent entry by M.

[2nd] [Δ%] [K] M [=] — calculates the percentage change (Δ%) between each subsequent entry x_1 and M, where:

$$\Delta \% = \frac{x_1 - M}{M} \times 100$$

(First entry) [+] [K] M [%] [=] —adds M% of any entry to that entry.
(First entry) [−] [K] M [%] [=] —subtracts M% of any entry from that entry.

Example: Multiply 2, 4, and 7 by 3.1416.

Procedure	Press	Display
1. Enter first value.	2	**2**
2. Set constant calculation.	[×] [K] 3.1416	**3.1416**
3. Calculate result.	[=]	**6.2832**
4. Calculate second result.	4 [=]	**12.5664**
5. Calculate third result.	7 [=]	**21.9912**

Example: Add 5% tax to each of the following prices with the answer rounded to the nearest penny: $5.95, $19.98, and $129.75.

Procedure	Press	Display
1. Select two decimal places.	[FIX] 2	**0.00**
2. Enter first value.	5.95	**5.95**
3. Set constant calculation.	[+] [K] 5 [%]	**0.30**
4. Calculate result.	[=]	**6.25**
5. Calculate second result.	19.98 [=]	**20.98**
6. Calculate third result.	129.75 [=]	**136.24**

The constant value and math operation are saved by the *Constant Memory*™ feature when you turn the calculator off. When you turn the calculator on again, press [ON/C] only one time if you want to retain the constant (pressing [ON/C] twice clears the constant). Pressing another operation key or [ON/C] after [K], also changes or clears the constant.

IMPORTANT: Although you can set the constant function in all modes, there are some limitations. The constant is cleared in the financial mode wnen any financial computation is performed. The constant is also cleared in the statistical mode when any variable is entered. Since the constant number is stored in the y register, using [x:y] can cause erroneous results.

Memory Keys — [STO], [RCL], [SUM], [EXC]

The memory in your calculator is a special storage register that can hold a number you may need to use in problems later on. You can store numbers and add to what's in memory without affecting any other calculations you may have in progress. The memory content is not changed by [ON/C], [2nd] [Mode], [2nd] [CMR], or [OFF].

[STO] — The Store Key "stores" the displayed number in the memory, without removing it from the display. (Any number previously stored in memory is lost.) Press [ON/C] [STO] to clear the memory by storing a zero.

[RCL] — By pressing the Recall Key any time after a number is stored in memory, the number reappears in the display and can be used in operations and calculations. The number remains in the memory after you press the [RCL] key and can be recalled as many times as you need. The number will remain in memory until you alter it with one of the other memory keys.

[SUM] — This key allows you to add whatever's in the display to the value in the memory, without affecting any calculation in progress. The [SUM] key comes in handy when you want to keep a running total on something (your expense account, for example), while keeping the rest of the calculator clear for other things (like gas mileage or shared expenses). *Note*: To ensure that the previous memory content does not affect your calculation, always use [STO] to store the first quantity of a new problem or press [ON/C] [STO] to clear the memory.

[EXC] — The Exchange Key "swaps" what's stored in memory with what's in the display. (The display value is stored, while the stored number is recalled.)

Example: Store 5.6 in memory and add 8.7. Enter 12.8 and exchange it with the result in memory. Recall 12.8.

Procedure	Press	Display	Memory
1. Store first value.	5.6 [STO]	**5.6**	5.6
2. Add second value to first.	8.7 [SUM]	**8.7**	14.3
3. Enter third value and exchange with result.	12.8 [EXC]	**14.30**	12.8
4. Recall third value.	[RCL]	**12.80**	12.8

Mode Keys — [2nd] [Mode], [2nd] [CMR]

Your calculator operates in three different modes: profit margin, financial, or statistical. Press [2nd] [Mode] repeatedly until the appropriate indicator appears in the display.

- Financial — "FIN" shows in the display.
- Statistical — "STAT" shows in the display.
- Profit margin — No mode indicator shows in the display.

Each of the above "activates" certain keys. Keys which are unique to one mode do NOT work when the calculator is in another mode. When the calculator is in one mode, pressing a key unique to another mode causes "Error" to be displayed. Also, data which is entered in one mode cannot be transferred to another mode.

To clear all data stored in the mode registers, press [2nd] [CMR]. All previously entered data and intermediate results in the mode registers are also cleared by pressing [2nd] [Mode].

Cost, Selling Price, and Gross Profit Margin Keys — CST, SEL, MAR

To use any of these keys, your calculator must be in profit margin mode. Press 2nd Mode until neither "FIN" nor "STAT" appear in the display.

One of the features of your calculator is its special handling of cost, selling price, and profit margin problems. These three keys work together to compute the cost (CST), selling price (SEL), and gross profit margin (MAR) on retail merchandise. If you enter any two of the variables, the calculator can compute the third one for you. To enter data, press the first function of a key:

CST — enters the displayed value as the cost of an item
SEL — enters the displayed value as the selling price of an item
MAR — enters the displayed value as the profit margin in percent

To find the missing variable, press the appropriate second function:

2nd CST — computes the cost of an item after the selling price and profit margin have been entered

2nd SEL — computes the selling price after the cost and profit margin have been entered

2nd MAR — computes the profit margin after the cost and selling price have been entered

Calculations are based on the equation

$$\text{Profit Margin (\%)} = \frac{\text{Sell} - \text{Cost}}{\text{Sell}} \times 100$$

Compound Interest Calculations (Single Sum) — N, %i, PV, FV

When performing compound interest calculations, select the financial mode by pressing 2nd Mode until "FIN" appears in the display. The four basic elements of compound interest computations are:

N — The total number of compounding periods,
%i — The percent interest per compounding period,
PV — The present value (what your money is worth today),
FV — The future value (what your money will be worth in the future).

Enter the three known values. Then press 2nd and the key for the unknown value, and the calculator solves the compound interest problem for you. (For compound interest calculations, the payment must be zero.)

Annuity Problems (Series of Equal Payments) — N, %i, PMT, PV, FV

Your calculator recognizes an annuity calculation when PMT (the Payment Key) is used with the other financial keys. The calculator will solve for the unknown value in ordinary annuity or annuity due computations when you enter *any three of the known values*. (Ordinary annuities are equal payment situations where payments are made at the *end* of a specified period. Annuities due occur when payments are made at the *beginning* of the period.) To work annuity calculations, your calculator should be in the financial mode; press 2nd Mode until "FIN" appears in the display.

The basic elements of an annuity problem are:

N — The total number of payment periods,
%i — The interest per payment period,
PMT — The amount of the regular payment,
PV — The present value of a series of payments when considering savings, or the loan amount when considering loans,
FV — The future value of a series of payments.

Your calculator is capable of directly solving annuity problems involving either a present value or a future value, but not both. If both PV and FV are entered in an annuity calculation, the calculator uses the last entered value (PV or FV) to solve for the unknown value. For example, if the future value variable is the only or the last variable entered of PV and FV, your calculator will ignore the value in the present value data register and proceed to solve the problem as a future value annuity problem.

After you enter the three known values, you solve for the unknown by pressing 2nd (for an ordinary annuity) or DUE (for an annuity due), followed by the key for the variable you are computing.

IMPORTANT: The calculator blanks the display while performing calculations. Keyboard entries are ignored when the display is blanked even though symbols or digits may appear while some keys are pressed. The computation for %i may typically take 5 to 30 seconds. If unrealistic values are entered for computation of %i, the calculating time may be minutes or even hours. If this occurs, press OFF and then ON/C twice to go on to another calculation.

The following two key descriptions cover special amortization functions. The information that must be in place before using these functions is the percent interest ([%i]), the payment amount ([PMT]), the present value ([PV]) or loan amount, and the number of periods ([N]). Enter three variables, then compute the fourth before using the following functions.

Principal and Interest Key — [2nd] [P/I]

For any payment number entered in the display, this key sequence determines the principal amount of that payment for a fully amortized, direct-reduction loan. After the principal is displayed, press [x:y] to display the amount of interest included in that payment. The calculator must be in financial mode ("FIN" shows in display) for calculations involving the [2nd] [P/I] key sequence.

Accumulated Interest and Loan Balance Key — [2nd] [Acc/Bal]

This key sequence finds the accumulated interest paid from the first payment through the payment number entered in the display (inclusive). Then pressing [x:y] displays the balance remaining on the loan principal after the specified payment. When you use the [2nd] [Acc/Bal] key sequence, the calculator must be in the financial mode ("FIN" shows in display).

Follow this procedure to calculate the accumulated interest paid from the Mth through the Nth payments, inclusive:

- Enter Nth payment number, press [2nd] [Acc/Bal], wait for result, then press [STO].
- Enter Mth payment number, press [2nd] [Acc/Bal], wait for result, then press [+/-] [SUM].
- Press [RCL] to display accumulated interest.

A Note about Financial Calculations

When you attempt to perform financial calculations with *unrealistic* values, the display usually shows "Error." However, there are *isolated* cases where the calculator does not detect unrealistic values. For example, if you compute N (number of periods) with a loan amount (PV) of $30,000, an annual interest rate (%i) of 10% compounded annually, and annual payments (PMT) of $3,000, the calculator displays a result of 241.58858. This problem is unrealistic since each payment of $3,000 is exactly equal to the interest due ($30,000 × 10% = $3,000). Therefore, the principal of $30,000 would never be paid.

Statistical Data Entry and Removal Keys — Σ+, 2nd Σ-

These keys are only functional when the calculator is in the statistical mode. Press 2nd Mode until "STAT" appears in the display.

Σ+ — Enters data points for statistical calculations. After you enter a data point, the calculator displays the current total number (n) of data points entered.

The mode registers retain all entered data even after you turn the calculator off. This means you can enter additional data points to a previously entered data array without having to reenter the old data first.

2nd Σ- — The Data Removal Key Sequence removes unwanted data points from the stored data array. After a data point is removed, the calculator displays the current total number (n) of data points stored.

The procedures to enter and remove an array of data are provided in the following chart.

SINGLE-VARIABLE DATA	TWO-VARIABLE DATA
1. To Enter Data Points:	
■ Enter first data point ■ Press Σ+ ■ Repeat for all data points	■ Enter first "x" data point ■ Press x:y ■ Enter first "y" data point ■ Press Σ+ ■ Repeat for all points
2. To Remove Last Data Point Entered*:	
■ Press 2nd Σ-	■ Press 2nd Σ-
3. To Remove Any Other Data Point Entered:	
■ Press ON/C x:y ■ Enter unwanted data point ■ Press 2nd Σ- ■ Repeat for other unwanted data points	■ Enter first unwanted "x" data point ■ Press x:y ■ Enter first unwanted "y" data point ■ Press 2nd Σ- ■ Repeat for other unwanted "x" and "y" data points

*If any statistical computation has been performed, you must use the third procedure.

Once entered, the data can be used to calculate the mean, variance, and standard deviation by simply pressing the necessary keys.

IMPORTANT: Since the calculator can hold statistical data in the mode registers even when turned off, always clear the registers with [2nd] [CMR] before entering a new set of statistical data.

Mean, Standard Deviation, and Variance Keys — [2nd] [Mean], [2nd] [σn], [2nd] [σn-1], [2nd] [σn] [x^2], [2nd] [σn-1] [x^2]

Before using any of these keys, press [2nd] [Mode] until "STAT" (statistical mode) appears in the display.

[2nd] [Mean] — Calculates the mean (average) of the data entered.

When you are calculating the standard deviation and variance, the keys you use depend on whether your data represents an entire population or a sample portion of the population.

[2nd] [σn] — Calculates the standard deviation with n weighting (for population data).

[2nd] [σn-1] — Calculates the standard deviation with n-1 weighting (for sample data).

[2nd] [σn] [x^2] — Calculates the variance of a population (with n weighting).

[2nd] [σn-1] [x^2] — Calculates the variance of a sample (with n-1 weighting).

NOTE: If you enter more than 30 data points, the difference between the standard deviation with n weighting and the standard deviation with n-1 weighting becomes very small.

A Look at the Keys

The various key sequences that may be used to analyze an array of statistical data are provided in the following chart.

SINGLE-VARIABLE DATA	TWO-VARIABLE DATA
■ Enter first data point ■ Press [Σ+]. ■ Repeat for all data points.	Call the two sets of data "x" (independent) and "y" (dependent) arrays of data. ■ Enter first "x" data point. ■ Press [x:y] ■ Enter first "y" data point. ■ Press [Σ+]. ■ Repeat for all points.
■ Press [2nd] [Mean] to calculate the mean of the data. ■ Press [2nd] [σ_{n-1}] to calculate the standard deviation of the data using n−1 weighting (normally used for *sample* data). ■ Press [2nd] [σ_n] to calculate the standard deviation of the data using n weighting. ■ Press [2nd] [σ_{n-1}] [x^2] to calculate the variance of the data (with n-1 weighting). ■ Press [2nd] [σ_n] [x^2] to calculate the variance of the data with n weighting.	■ Press [2nd] [Mean] to calculate the mean of the "y" data points. Then press [x:y] to display the mean of the "x" data points. ■ Press [2nd] [σ_{n-1}] to calculate the standard deviation of the "y" data using n-1 weighting. Then press [x:y] to display the standard deviation of the "x" data using n-1 weighting. ■ Press [2nd] [σ_{n-1}] [x^2] to calculate the variance of the "y" data points with n-1 weighting. Then press [x:y] to display the variance of the "x" data points with n−1 weighting. ■ Press [2nd] [σ_n] to calculate the standard deviation of the "y" data points using n weighting. Then press [x:y] to display the standard deviation of the "x" data points using n weighting. ■ Press [2nd] [σ_n] [x^2] to calculate the variance of the "y" data points with n weighting. Then press [x:y] [x^2] to calculate the variance of the "x" data points with n weighting.

Example: Enter the three data points, 96, 85, and 57, and find the mean.

Procedure	Press		Display
1. Clear calculator and mode registers; select floating decimal point.	[ON/C] [2nd] [CMR] [FIX] 8		**0**
2. Select statistical mode ("STAT" shows in display).	[2nd] [Mode]	STAT	**0**
3. Enter first data point.	96 [Σ+]	STAT	**1**
4. Enter second data point *incorrectly.*	88 [Σ+]	STAT	**2**
5. Remove incorrect data point.	[2nd] [Σ-]	STAT	**1**
6. Enter second data point correctly.	85 [Σ+]	STAT	**2**
7. Enter third data point.	57 [Σ+]	STAT	**3**
8. Compute mean.	[2nd] [Mean]	STAT	**79.333333**

Example: Enter the three data points, 81, 76, and 98, and find the mean.

Procedure	Press		Display
1. Clear calculator and mode registers; select floating decimal point.	[ON/C] [2nd] [CMR] [FIX] 8		**0**
2. Select statistical mode ("STAT" shows in display).	[2nd] [Mode]	STAT	**0**
3. Enter first data point.	81 [Σ+]	STAT	**1**
4. Enter second data point *incorrectly.*	66 [Σ+]	STAT	**2**
5. Enter third data point.	98 [Σ+]	STAT	**3**
6. Remove incorrect data point.	[ON/C] [x:y] 66 [2nd] [Σ-]	STAT	**2**
7. Enter correct data point.	76 [Σ+]	STAT	**3**
8. Compute mean.	[2nd] [Mean]	STAT	**85**

Linear Regression and Trend Line Analysis Keys — [2nd] [b/a], [2nd] [x'], [2nd] [y'], [2nd] [Corr]

Linear regression is useful for analyzing historical data and using the results to project future information. The data points you know are entered by their "x" and "y" coordinates using the two-variable data entry procedure described at the beginning of this section.

Trend line analysis is a variation of linear regression that's very handy in making predictions based on trends or growth. In trend line analysis, the "x" values are automatically increased by 1 for each data point. Your calculator does this for you all by itself — all you need to do is enter the first "x" value with the [x:y] key, and then enter consecutive "y" values with the [Σ+] key. The calculator automatically increments the "x" variable by one for each "y" value you enter. If an error is made in data entry, simply press [2nd] [Σ-] to remove the incorrect entry before making another entry.

In both linear regression and trend line analysis situations, your calculator is mathematically drawing a straight line graph through the series of data points entered into the machine. The actual placement of the line is determined by a least-squares linear regression that minimizes the sum of the squares of the deviation of the y values from the straight line of best fit. The linear equation of the form $y = ax + b$ is determined for the line.

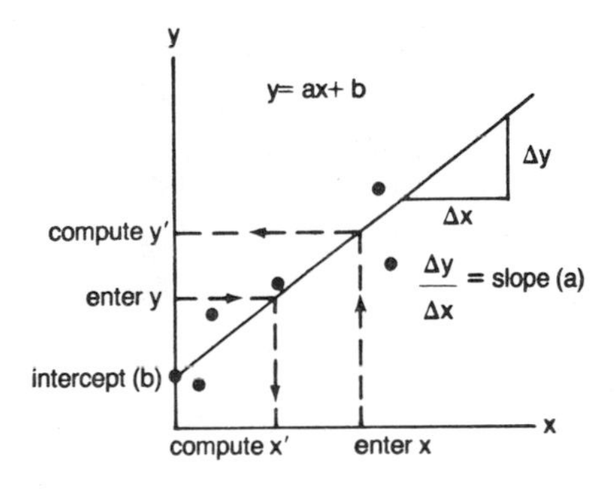

2nd b/a — The Intercept and Slope Key Sequence calculates the y-intercept (b) of the line. After the y-intercept is displayed, press x:y to see the slope (a) of the line.

2nd x′ — This key sequence finds the x′ value for a given y value on the calculated regression line.

2nd y′ — This key sequence calculates the y′ value for a given x value on the calculated regression line.

2nd Corr — Calculates the correlation coefficient of the data entered in the linear regression routine. This value will fall between -1 and +1. The closer the result to ±1, the better the existing correlation is. A value of zero (0) means that no correlation exists between the data points.

After you enter your two-variable data, the following keystroke sequences can be used to find the linear regression or trend line analysis information you want.

INFORMATION WANTED	KEY SEQUENCE
■ y-intercept (b)	■ Press 2nd b/a
■ slope of line (a)	■ Press 2nd b/a x:y
■ y′ value for a given x value	■ Enter x and press 2nd y′
■ x′ value for a given y value	■ Enter y and press 2nd x′
■ Correlation coefficient	■ Press 2nd Corr

NOTE: If the line is vertical, no y-intercept exists and the slope is undefinable. Calculating the slope will yield an error condition and additional "x" points cannot be predicted. If the line is horizontal, the slope is 0 and new "y" values cannot be predicted.

Example: No Die Life Insurance Company has found that the volume of sales (y) varies according to the number of sales people employed (x).

Number of salespeople (x)	7	12	3	5	11	8	9
Sales in thousands/mo. (y)	99	152	81	98	151	112	?

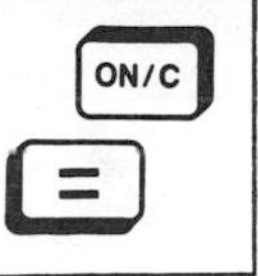

Procedure	Press		Display
1. Clear calculator and mode registers; select floating decimal point.	[ON/C] [2nd] [CMR] [FIX] 8		0
2. Select statistical mode ("STAT" shows in display).	[2nd] [Mode]	STAT	0
3. Enter first pair of data points.	7 [x:y] 99 [Σ+]	STAT	1
4. Enter second pair of data points.	12 [x:y] 152 [Σ+]	STAT	2
5. Enter third pair of data points.	3 [x:y] 81 [Σ+]	STAT	3
6. Enter fourth pair of data points.	5 [x:y] 98 [Σ+]	STAT	4
7. Enter fifth pair of data points.	11 [x:y] 151 [Σ+]	STAT	5
8. Enter sixth pair of data points.	8 [x:y] 112 [Σ+]	STAT	6
9. Enter known x value and solve for y value.	9 [2nd] [y']	STAT	126.60112

"ERROR" Indications

The display shows "Error" when an overflow or underflow occurs, or when an improper operation or key sequence is attempted. When an "Error" condition occurs, no entry from the keyboard (except [OFF]) will be accepted until [ON/C] is pressed. This clears the "Error" condition and any pending calculation. (See *Appendix B* for a list of the causes of "Error" conditions).

Clear "Error" condition. In general, pressing [ON/C] when "Error" is displayed clears the display and any pending arithmetic calculation. If the "Error" condition resulted from a user memory overflow or underflow, the user memory is also cleared. If the "Error" condition resulted from a mode register overflow or underflow, or from a computational error pertaining to the statistical or financial modes, the mode registers are cleared when you press [ON/C].

CHAPTER

2 PRICING AND PROFIT

You encounter situations involving pricing and profit every day. When you are buying merchandise, the final purchase price is affected by sales taxes, discounts, and markups. On the other side of the transaction, the selling price of the merchandise is determined by the amount the merchant paid (cost) and the merchant's gross profit margin (GPM) or markup.

Note that the *gross profit margin* differs from a *markup*. As used in this book, a GPM is a percentage of the selling price and is calculated using the formula:

$$\text{Profit Margin (\%)} = \frac{\text{Sell} - \text{Cost}}{\text{Sell}} \times 100$$

In contrast, a markup is a percentage of the cost. The term markup, as we've used it, is equivalent to "add-on" and markdown means the same as "discount." Sample problems involving both GPM and markup/markdown are illustrated in this chapter. An example of the Cost-Volume-Profit analysis technique, which merchants apply to determine the breakeven point and the sales level necessary to earn a given income after taxes, is also included.

Your calculator has special keys for performing quick and accurate calculations related to pricing and profit: [%], [CST], [SEL], and [MAR]. With this capability at your fingertips, you can concentrate on making the sale and increasing the profit potential of your business. Or if you're the consumer, your calculator can give you a breakdown of your expenses.

Determining Sales Tax and Price

You are buying a new sorting machine from a local business supply store and have agreed on a price of $4632, plus 4% sales tax. How much will the tax and the total cost be?

Procedure	Press	Display
1. Clear calculator and select two decimal places.	[ON/C] [FIX] 2	**0.00**
2. Enter purchase price.	4632	**4632**
3. Calculate amount of sales tax.	[+] 4 [%]	**185.28**
4. Calculate total cost.	[=]	**4817.28**

The sales tax is $185.28 and the total cost is $4817.28.

Determining Price Before Sales Tax

You and a salesman have just agreed that the final price you'll pay for a refrigerator is $550.00, which includes the 6% sales tax. How much are you paying for the refrigerator, and how much is paid in taxes?

Procedure	Press	Display
1. Clear calculator and select two decimal places.	[ON/C] [FIX] 2	**0.00**
2. Add 1 and tax percent.	1 [+] 6 [%] [=]	**1.06**
3. Calculate reciprocal of displayed number.	[1/x]	**0.94**
4. Multiply by final price to calculate selling price.	[×] 550 [=]	**518.87**
5. Calculate amount of tax.	[×] 6 [%] [=]	**31.13**

The price of the refrigerator is $518.87 and the tax is $31.13.

CHAPTER 2

Discounts and Sales Tax

A store near your home recently advertised a lawnmower, which usually sells for $239.45, at a 15% discount. What is the sale price?

Procedure	Press	Display
1. Clear calculator and select two decimal places.	[ON/C] [FIX] 2	0.00
2. Enter regular price.	239.45	239.45
3. Subtract discount rate to calculate sale price.	[−] 15 [%] [=]	**203.53**

The sale price of the lawnmower is $203.53.

Determining Price Before Discount

A stereo system is on sale for $323.55. The salesman explains that the sale price is a 35% savings from the regular price. What is the regular price?

Procedure	Press	Display
1. Clear calculator and select two decimal places.	[ON/C] [FIX] 2	0.00
2. Subtract percent savings from 1.	1 [−] 35 [%] [=]	0.65
3. Calculate reciprocal of displayed number.	[1/x]	1.54
4. Multiply by the sale price to calculate the regular price.	[×] 323.55 [=]	**497.77**

The price was $497.77 before discount.

Determining Cost Before Markup

The list price of a certain microwave oven is $342.56, and the store's markup is 22% of cost. How much did the microwave oven cost the store?

Procedure	Press	Display
1. Clear calculator and select two decimal places.	[ON/C] [FIX] 2	**0.00**
2. Add 1 and markup percent.	1 [+] 22 [%] [=]	**1.22**
3. Calculate reciprocal of displayed number.	[1/x]	**0.82**
4. Multiply by list price to calculate cost.	[×] 342.56 [=]	**280.79**

The cost of the oven to the store was $280.79.

Markups and Selling Prices

A grocery store manager has purchased a load of bananas for $0.21 per pound. At what price should he sell the bananas if his standard markup is 20% of cost?

Procedure	Press	Display
1. Clear calculator and select two decimal places.	[ON/C] [FIX] 2	**0.00**
2. Enter cost per pound.	.21	**0.21**
3. Add markup percentage to determine selling price.	[+] 20 [%] [=]	**0.25**

The selling price should be $0.25 per pound.

CHAPTER 2

What Selling Price Is Necessary to Earn a Specified GPM?

You need to determine the retail price for an item that cost your store $22.50. If you require a 35% gross profit margin on sales, what should the retail price be?

Procedure	Press	Display
1. Clear calculator and mode registers.* Select two decimal places.	[ON/C] [2nd] [CMR] [FIX] 2	**0.00**
2. Select profit-margin mode ("FIN" or "STAT" does *not* show in the display).	[2nd] [Mode]	**0.00**
3. Enter cost.	22.50 [CST]	**22.50**
4. Enter percentage of gross profit margin.	35 [MAR]	**35.00**
5. Calculate selling price.	[2nd] [SEL]	**34.62**

The retail price should be $34.62.

*For correct results when using the keys unique to any of the three modes (profit-margin, financial, statistical), be sure to clear the mode registers ([2nd] [CMR]) when you clear the calculator's display ([ON/C]).

Determining Percent Markup

A store is selling stereo speakers for $42.50 each. The wholesale cost of the speakers was $31.23 each. What is the percentage of markup based on the cost?

Procedure	Press	Display
1. Clear calculator and select two decimal places.	[ON/C] [FIX] 2	**0.00**
2. Enter selling price.	42.50	**42.50**
3. Calculate percentage of markup on cost.	[2nd] [Δ%] 31.23 [=]	**36.09**

The markup from cost is about 36%.

Calculating the Dealer's Cost, Based on GPM

A new compact car on a showroom floor has a base sticker price of $5100. You read in a consumer magazine that compacts are generally priced to provide the dealer about a 17% margin on the selling price. If this report is correct, how much did the car cost the dealer?

Procedure	Press	Display
1. Clear calculator and mode registers; select two decimal places.	[ON/C] [2nd] [CMR] [FIX] 2	**0.00**
2. Select profit-margin mode ("FIN" or "STAT" does *not* show in the display).	[2nd] [Mode]	**0.00**
3. Enter selling price.	5100 [SEL]	**5100.00**
4. Enter margin.	17 [MAR]	**17.00**
5. Calculate cost.	[2nd] [CST]	**4233.00**

Assuming a 17% margin, the cost was $4233.

CHAPTER 2

Determining the Amount a Store Will Pay for a Product, Based on GPM

You are manufacturing a fertilizer spreader retailed by a local store for $24.50. The store requires a GPM of 30% of sales on all merchandise. What is the maximum price you can charge the store for your product?

Procedure	Press	Display
1. Clear calculator and mode registers; select two decimal places.	ON/C 2nd CMR FIX 2	0.00
2. Select profit-margin mode ("FIN" or "STAT" does *not* show in the display).	2nd Mode	0.00
3. Enter retail price.	24.50 SEL	**24.50**
4. Enter margin.	30 MAR	**30.00**
5. Calculate cost.	2nd CST	**17.15**

The highest price the store will be willing to pay is $17.15 per unit.

Calculating Margin (GPM)

You are making macrame bags, and your total material, labor, and incidental costs per bag are $13.75. A local store pays you $17.47 for each bag you make. What is your gross profit margin (GPM) on selling price?

Procedure	Press	Display
1. Clear calculator and mode registers; select two decimal places.	[ON/C] [2nd] [CMR] [FIX] 2	0.00
2. Select profit-margin mode ("FIN" or "STAT" does *not* show in the display).	[2nd] [Mode]	0.00
3. Enter selling price.	17.47 [SEL]	17.47
4. Enter cost.	13.75 [CST]	13.75
5. Calculate GPM.	[2nd] [MAR]	**21.29**

Your GPM is 21.29%.

CHAPTER **2**

Cost-Volume-Profit Analysis

A canoe company sells its paddles for $20 each. The unit variable cost is $15, and fixed costs are $3,000. The company's tax rate is 40%. Assuming that all paddles produced are sold and all costs remain the same, what sales volume (in dollars and units) must be reached to earn $2,500 after taxes? What after-tax income will be produced by $34,000 in sales? What is the breakeven point in sales dollars and units necessary to earn the required profit on the sale?

Procedure	Press	Display
1. Clear calculator and select two decimal places.	[ON/C] [STO] [FIX] 2	**0.00**
2. Divide unit cost by selling price.	15 [÷] 20 [=]	**0.75**
3. Subtract displayed number from 1 to calculate contribution margin as a decimal; store result.	[+/−] [+] 1 [=] [STO]	**0.25**
4. Solve for sales to reach desired income.		
a. Subtract tax rate from 1.	1 [−] 40 [%] [=]	**0.60**
b. Find reciprocal of displayed number and multiply by desired income to calculate income before taxes.	[1/x] [×] 2500 [=]	**4166.67**
c. Add fixed costs.	[+] 3000 [=]	**7166.67**
d. Divide by contribution margin stored in memory to determine sales volume in dollars.	[÷] [RCL] [=]	**28666.67**
e. Divide by sales price to find sales volume in units.	[÷] 20 [=]	**1433.33**

Procedure	Press	Display
5. Solve for income produced by specified sales.		
a. Multiply sales in dollars by contribution margin.	34000 [×] [RCL] [=]	**8500.00**
b. Calculate income before tax by deducting fixed costs.	[−] 3000 [=]	**5500.00**
c. Calculate after-tax income using company's tax rate.	[−] 40 [%] [=]	**3300.00**
6. Solve for breakeven point.		
a. Enter fixed costs.	3000	**3000**
b. Divide by contribution margin to find breakeven point in dollars.	[÷] [RCL] [=]	**12000.00**
c. Divide by sales price to calculate breakeven point in units.	[÷] 20 [=]	**600.00**

The necessary sales volume is $28,666.67 or 1,433 units; the after-tax income is $3,300.00; and the breakeven point is $12,000.00 in sales or 600 units.

Reference:

Horngren, *Cost Accounting: A Managerial Emphasis,* pp. 62-63.

CHAPTER 3

INTEREST

One of the most fascinating (and sometimes troublesome) aspects of using money is that it both earns and costs. That is, you can invest your money in a growth situation so that it earns additional money (interest), or you can borrow from a lending agency, in which case you must pay (interest) for the use of someone else's money. Almost every day, you have to make decisions about money in your personal or professional life. Sound financial planning calls for a close look at the way money works and the alternatives that are available to you.

The amount of interest paid depends on four factors:

1. The amount of money involved (called principal)
2. The interest rate (usually expressed as a percentage per time unit)
3. The length of time the money is borrowed or loaned
4. The type of interest (or the way the interest is computed)

In this chapter, we'll explore several ways of calculating interest and interest rate conversions. We've also included examples involving continuous interest rates and situations where the number of compounding periods differs from the number of payment periods. For either of these, it's sometimes necessary to convert the given interest rate to an equivalent rate; *Appendix A* lists the formulas used in the conversion routines. Also, since many of the applications involve specialized terminology, each new term is briefly explained in the example where it's used the first time.

Simple Interest

Suppose you deposit $1000 at 6% annual simple interest for three years. How much money would you have at the end of three years?

The formula for computing simple interest is:

Simple Interest = Principal × Interest Rate × Time

Procedure	Press	Display
1. Clear calculator and select two decimal places.	[ON/C] [FIX] 2	**0.00**
2. Enter principal.	1000	**1000**
3. Calculate interest earned in one year.	[×] 6 [%] [=]	**60.00**
4. Calculate interest earned in three years.	[×] 3 [=]	**180.00**
5. Add principal to calculate total amount (principal + interest) at end of time period.	[+] 1000 [=]	**1180.00**

You would have $1180.00 at the end of three years.

Notice that simple interest is earned on the original amount of principal only. In simple interest situations, the amount of interest you earn depends not only on the interest rate, but on the way time is calculated for interest periods. For instance, a year may be assumed to contain 360 days or the actual number of calendar days in the year. You need to check with the agency or persons involved when making such calculations.

CHAPTER
3 Compound Interest

Most borrowing, lending and savings situations involve compound interest. With a savings account, compound interest means that interest is earned not only on the original amount of principal, but also on the *interest* that you have earned in each previous compounding period and left in the account. In the borrowing situation, compound interest means that you pay interest only on the unpaid balance, not on the original principal borrowed. For instance, let's consider the previous example, but with yearly compounding.

You deposit $1000 at an annual interest rate of 6% compounded annually for three years. Assuming the interest earned is left in the account, how much money will you have at the end of the third year?

Procedure	Press	Display
1. Clear calculator and select two decimal places.	[ON/C] [FIX] 2	**0.00**
2. Add interest to original principal amount to calculate amount you'll have after one year.	1000 [+] 6 [%] [=]	**1060.00**
3. Add interest to previous amount to calculate amount you'll have after two years.	[+] 6 [%] [=]	**1123.60**
4. Add interest to previous amount to calculate amount you'll have after three years.	[+] 6 [%] [=]	**1191.02**

You would have $1191.02 at the end of three years.

The method used above illustrates how interest is compounded manually. Your calculator, however, has special keys to make computation of compound interest easy.

- [N] key — Enters or computes the number of compounding periods.
- [%i] key — Enters or computes the interest rate per compounding period.
- [PV] key — Enters or computes the present value of the investment.
- [FV] key — Enters or computes the future value.
- [2nd] key — Used in conjunction with the above keys to compute the unknown variable.

NOTE: In compound interest situations, the payment must be zero; this is the only way the calculator recognizes the difference between compound interest and annuity problems. Also, all calculations involving the financial keys should begin with [2nd] [CMR] to clear the financial memories.

Now, let's work the previous example again, using these keys.

Procedure	Press		Display
1. Clear calculator and mode registers; select two decimal places.	[ON/C] [2nd] [CMR] [FIX] 2		**0.00**
2. Select financial mode ("FIN" shows in the display).	[2nd] [Mode]	FIN	**0.00**
3. Enter number of compounding periods (years, in this case).	3 [N]	FIN	**3.00**
4. Enter interest rate per compounding period (annual, in this case).	6 [%i]	FIN	**6.00**
5. Enter principal amount as present value.	1000 [PV]	FIN	**1000.00**
6. Compute future value.	[2nd] [FV]	FIN	**1191.02**

Notice that this answer agrees with the previous result and that the keystroke sequence used here is easier, particularly for a large number of compounding periods.

CHAPTER 3

Which Annual Nominal Interest Rate is Better?

Assume that Bank A quotes an Annual Percent Interest Rate (APR) of 5.5% compounded quarterly and Bank B quotes an APR of 5.5% compounded monthly. You are planning to deposit $10,000 for two years. Which bank will pay more, and how much more will it pay?

Interest rates are often specified as an annual rate with daily, monthly, quarterly, or semiannual compounding; for instance, 18% *annual* interest compounded monthly. This annual rate is called the *nominal* interest rate and it tells you the interest rate for a specified period of time, usually a year. To determine the periodic compounding rate (in this case, the monthly rate), 18% is divided by 12 (the number of months in a year) to give you a monthly interest rate of 1.5%.

Annual Percent Interest Rate (APR) is another term often used by lending institutions. APR is generally the same as the annual nominal interest rate. The APR divided by the number of compounding periods per year equals the interest rate per compounding period.

Procedure	Press		Display
1. Clear calculator and mode registers; select two decimal places.	[ON/C] [STO] [2nd] [CMR] [FIX] 2		**0.00**
2. Select financial mode ("FIN" shows in the display).	[2nd] [Mode]	FIN	**0.00**
3. Enter amount invested.	10000 [PV]	FIN	**10000.00**

Which Annual Nominal Interest Rate is Better?

$/$

Procedure	Press		Display
4. Evaluate Bank A.			
a. Calculate and enter total number of compounding periods.*	2 [×] 4 [=] [N]	FIN	**8.00**
b. Calculate and enter interest rate per compounding period (quarterly).	5.5 [÷] 4 [=] [%i]	FIN	**1.38**
c. Compute and store account balance for comparison with Bank B.	[2nd] [FV] [STO]	FIN	**11154.42**
5. Evaluate Bank B.			
a. Enter number of compounding periods.	2 [×] 12 [=] [N]	FIN	**24.00**
b. Enter interest rate per compounding period (monthly).	5.5 [÷] 12 [=] [%i]	FIN	**0.46**
c. Compute account balance.	[2nd] [FV]	FIN	**11159.98**
6. Subtract Bank A's balance from Bank B's to calculate difference.	[−] [RCL] [=]	FIN	**5.56**

Bank B will pay $5.56 more interest than Bank A.

*The number of compounding periods equals the number of years times the number of compounding periods per year.

CHAPTER 3

Converting Nominal Rates to Annual Effective Interest Rates

In the previous example, Bank A and Bank B both paid a 5.5% annual nominal interest rate, but they compounded the money a different number of times per year. Another way to compare the two banks would be to compute the *annual effective interest rate* paid by each bank. In other words, what equivalent interest rate compounded annually equals a nominal rate of 5.5% compounded quarterly or monthly?

An annual effective rate is the equivalent interest rate at which interest is actually compounded for a year.

Nominal interest rates are converted to annual effective rates as follows:

1. Use the nominal rate given to find the future value of $1 after one year.
2. With the number of compounding periods equal to 1 (one) and the future value just calculated, compute the effective rate (%i).

Procedure	Press		Display
1. Clear calculator and mode registers; select two decimal places.	[ON/C] [STO] [2nd] [CMR] [FIX] 2		**0.00**
2. Select financial mode ("FIN" shows in the display).	[2nd] [Mode]	FIN	**0.00**
3. Convert Bank A's rate to an annual effective rate.			
a. Enter number of compounding periods per year.	4 [N]	FIN	**4.00**
b. Calculate and enter interest rate per compounding period (quarterly).	5.5 [÷] 4 [=] [%i]	FIN	**1.38**
c. Enter 1 (one) for present value.	1 [PV]	FIN	**1.00**
d. Compute future value.	[2nd] [FV]	FIN	**1.06**

Converting Nominal Rates to Annual Effective Interest Rates

$/$

Procedure	Press		Display
e. Enter 1 (one) for number of compounding periods.	1 [N]	FIN	**1.00**
f. Compute annual effective rate.	[2nd] [%i]	FIN	**5.61**
5. Store result.	[STO]	FIN	**5.61**
6. Convert Bank B's rate to an annual effective rate.			
a. Enter number of compounding periods per year.	12 [N]	FIN	**12.00**
b. Calculate and enter interest rate per compounding period (monthly).	5.5 [÷] 12 [=] [%i]	FIN	**0.46**
c. Enter 1 (one) for present value.	1 [PV]	FIN	**1.00**
d. Compute future value.	[2nd] [FV]	FIN	**1.06**
e. Enter 1 (one) for number of compounding periods.	1 [N]	FIN	**1.00**
f. Compute annual effective rate.	[2nd] [%i]	FIN	**5.64**
7. Subtract Bank A's rate from Bank B's to calculate difference.	[-] [RCL] [=]	FIN	**0.03**

Bank B's annual effective interest rate exceeds Bank A's by 0.03%. This means that Bank B will pay more interest than Bank A, which agrees with the result from the previous example.

CHAPTER 3

Multiple Equal Deposits or Payments (Annuities)

At this point, we have only considered examples where one deposit was made. However, many everyday applications involve regular periodic deposits or payments. In this section we will discuss *annuities*—series of equal payments made at regular intervals of time. Two common types of annuities are *ordinary annuities* and *annuities due.*

To identify the type of annuity involved in an application, ask yourself, "When does each payment occur?"

- *Ordinary annuities* involve payments made at the end of each payment period. Most loans fall into this category.
- *Annuities due* involve payments made at the beginning of each payment period in anticipation of receiving some service or as part of an investment program. Most leases are annuity due situations.

Your calculator is equipped to handle both ordinary annuities and annuities due easily. The following keys on your calculator are used in calculations involving annnuities:

- [N] key — Enters or computes the total number of payment periods.
- [%i] key — Enters or computes the interest rate per payment period.
- [PMT] key — Enters or computes the amount of the periodic payment.
- [PV] key — Enters or computes the present value of the annuity.
- [FV] key — Enters or computes the future value.
- [DUE] key — Used in conjunction with the financial keys to compute the unknown value in an *annuity due* situation.
- [2nd] key — Used in conjunction with the financial keys to compute the unknown value in an *ordinary annuity* situation.

NOTE: Your calculator can directly solve annuity problems involving either a present value or a future value, but not both. For more information, see Chapter 1.

Determining the Amount of Annuity Payments

If you loan a friend $500 for three years at 6% annual interest, compounded monthly, how much should the monthly payments be to pay off the loan?

Your friend will make 36 monthly payments beginning a month after you loan him the money. Since the payments occur at the end of each payment period, this is an ordinary annuity situation.

Procedure	Press		Display
1. Clear calculator and mode registers; select two decimal places.	[ON/C] [2nd] [CMR] [FIX] 2		**0.00**
2. Select financial mode ("FIN" shows in the display).	[2nd] [Mode]	FIN	**0.00**
3. Enter number of payments.	36 [N]	FIN	**36.00**
4. Calculate and enter interest rate per payment period (monthly).	6 [÷] 12 [=] [%i]	FIN	**0.50**
5. Enter loan amount (present value).	500 [PV]	FIN	**500.00**
6. Calculate payment amount.	[2nd] [PMT]	FIN	**15.21**

You would receive payments of $15.21 each month.

Determining How Much Your Savings Will Be Worth If You Make Monthly Deposits

If your company deposits $6,000 at the beginning of each month in a savings account paying 6% annually, compounded monthly, what will the account balance be after seven months? Since the deposits are made at the beginning of each payment period, this is an annuity due situation.

	Procedure	Press		Display
1.	Clear calculator and mode registers; select two decimal places.	[ON/C] [2nd] [CMR] [FIX] 2		0.00
2.	Select financial mode ("FIN" shows in the display).	[2nd] [Mode]	FIN	0.00
3.	Enter number of payments.	7 [N]	FIN	7.00
4.	Calculate and enter interest rate per payment period (monthly).	6 [÷] 12 [=] [%i]	FIN	0.50
5.	Enter periodic deposit (payment) amount.	6000 [PMT]	FIN	6000.00
6.	**Calculate account balance (future value).**	[DUE] [FV]	FIN	**42848.45**

Determining How Much Your Savings Will Be Worth If You Make Monthly Deposits

(Do not clear your calculator.)
How much difference would it make if you made the deposit at the end of each month (ordinary annuity) rather than at the beginning (annuity due)? Try the following key sequence to find out.

Procedure	Press		Display
7. Store annuity due future value for later recall.	[STO]	FIN	**42848.45**
8. Compute future value based on an ordinary annuity situation.	[2nd] [FV]	FIN	**42635.27**
9. Compare the two values (first result - second result).	[+/−] [+] [RCL] [=]	FIN	**213.18**

By making the deposit at the beginning of each month instead of the end, you would earn $213.18 more after seven months.

CHAPTER 3 Finding the Future Value of an Annuity Where Compounding Periods and Payment Periods Are Not Equal

When you are saving or borrowing money, the number of payments or deposits you make per year may differ from the number of compounding periods per year. With your calculator, you can quickly convert the interest rate per compounding period to the equivalent interest rate per payment or deposit period as explained here:

1. Compute the future value of $1 after one year using the interest rate per compounding period and the number of compounding periods per year.
2. Keep this value, enter the number of payments per year, and compute the equivalent interest rate per payment period (%i).

Then enter the two other known values and solve for the unknown to complete the calculation.

You plan to deposit $1500 at the *beginning* of each quarter for three years. The savings account pays 6% annual interest, compounded monthly. How much will you have saved after three years? (*Note*: This is an annuity due situation since the deposits are made at the beginning of each quarter.)

Procedure	Press		Display
1. Clear calculator and mode registers; select two decimal places.	[ON/C] [2nd] [CMR] [FIX] 2		0.00
2. Select financial mode ("FIN" shows in the display).	[2nd] [Mode]	FIN	0.00

Finding the Future Value of an Annuity Where Compounding Periods and Payment Periods Are Not Equal

Procedure	Press		Display
3. Convert interest rate per compounding period to rate per payment period.			
a. Enter number of compounding periods per year.	12 [N]	FIN	**12.00**
b. Calculate and enter interest rate per compounding period (monthly).	6 [÷] 12 [=] [%i]	FIN	**0.50**
c. Enter 1 (one) for present value.	1 [PV]	FIN	**1.00**
d. Compute future value.	[2nd] [FV]	FIN	**1.06**
e. Enter number of payments per year.	4 [N]	FIN	**4.00**
f. Compute equivalent interest rate per payment period.	[2nd] [%i]	FIN	**1.51**
4. Calculate and enter total number of payments.	3 [×] 4 [=] [N]	FIN	**12.00**
5. Enter payment amount.	1500 [PMT]	FIN	**1500.00**
6. Compute future value of savings account.	[DUE] [FV]	FIN	**19865.06**

You will have $19,865.06 in the savings account after three years.

CHAPTER 3 Determining the Interest Rate Where Compounding Periods and Payment Periods Are Not Equal

At the *end* of each month, your aunt has deposited $75 in a savings account that compounds interest quarterly. After five years her balance is $5400.79. What is the average annual interest rate paid by the bank during the five years? (*Note*: Since the deposits were made at the end of each month, this is an ordinary annuity situation.)

This problem can be easily solved as follows:

1. Compute the interest rate per payment period and then use the number of payments per year to calculate the future value of $1.
2. Use this new future value and the number of compounding periods per year to find the interest rate per compounding period (%i).

Procedure	Press		Display
1. Clear calculator and mode registers; select two decimal places.	[ON/C] [2nd] [CMR] [FIX] 2		**0.00**
2. Select financial mode ("FIN" shows in the display).	[2nd] [Mode]	FIN	**0.00**
3. Calculate and enter number of deposits.	5 [×] 12 [=] [N]	FIN	**60.00**
4. Enter amount of deposit.	75 [PMT]	FIN	**75.00**
5. Enter balance at end of period.	5400.79 [FV]	FIN	**5400.79**
6. Compute interest rate per payment period.	[2nd] [%i]	FIN	**0.60**

Procedure	Press		Display
7. Convert computed interest rate to interest rate per compounding period.			
a. Enter 0 (zero) for payment.	0 [PMT]	FIN	**0.00**
b. Enter 1 (one) for present value.	1 [PV]	FIN	**1.00**
c. Enter number of payments per year.	12 [N]	FIN	**12.00**
d. Compute future value.	[2nd] [FV]	FIN	**1.07**
e. Enter number of compounding periods per year.	4 [N]	FIN	**4.00**
f. Compute interest rate per compounding period.	[2nd] [%i]	FIN	**1.82**
8. Multiply by number of compounding periods per year to calculate annual interest rate.	[×] 4 [=]	FIN	**7.27**

Your aunt earned an annual interest rate of 7.27% compounded quarterly.

NOTE: The conversion technique shown here assumes that interest is paid for partial periods. For example, if you deposit money at the beginning of the second month in a quarter and the savings account compounds quarterly, this method assumes that the bank will pay interest for the two months remaining in the quarter. If the bank pays interest only on the amount which was in the account at the beginning of the quarter, the conversion method will not give accurate results.

CHAPTER 3 Comparing the Amount of Interest Earned with Discrete or Continuous Compounding

You have the choice of investing $5,000 in a savings account which pays 6% compounded quarterly or an account which pays the same rate, but compounds interest continuously. Which account will have accrued more interest at the end of 3 years?

Continuous compounding is now used by some savings and loan associations and banks when they are charging or paying interest. This method assumes that compounding occurs continuously over the time periods rather than at the end of each period. In contrast, discrete compounding means that a definite period of time, such as daily, monthly, quarterly, etc., is used to calculate the amount of interest earned or paid. If annual nominal rates are equal, continuous compounding pays the most on a savings account and charges the most on a loan.

To compare continuous and discrete interest rates, it's necessary to use conversion formulas that find equivalent rates. To convert an annual rate with continuous compounding to an equivalent rate with discrete compounding, the formula is

$$i = e^r - 1$$

where i is the equivalent annual discrete rate per compounding period, e is the natural antilogarithm, and r is the annual continuous rate. To convert a discrete rate to an equivalent rate compounded continuously, use

$$r = \ln (1 + i)$$

where r and i are in decimal form.

Procedure	Press		Display
1. Clear calculator and mode registers; select two decimal places.	[ON/C] [STO] [2nd] [CMR] [FIX] 2		**0.00**
2. Select financial mode ("FIN" shows in the display).	[2nd] [Mode]	FIN	**0.00**
3. Enter number of years for continuous compounding.	3 [N]	FIN	**3.00**

Comparing the Amount of Interest Earned with Discrete or Continuous Compounding

Procedure	Press		Display
4. Convert continuous interest rate to equivalent discrete rate.			
a. Enter continuous rate as a decimal.	6 [%]	FIN	**0.06**
b. Calculate equivalent discrete rate.	[2nd] [e^x] [−] 1 [=]	FIN	**0.06**
c. Convert to percent and enter as interest rate.	[×] 100 [=] [%i]	FIN	**6.18**
5. Enter amount of investment.	5000 [PV]	FIN	**5000.00**
6. Compute and store account balance.	[2nd] [FV] [STO]	FIN	**5986.09**
7. Calculate and enter number of periods for quarterly compounding.	3 [×] 4 [=] [N]	FIN	**12.00**
8. Calculate and enter quarterly interest rate.	6 [÷] 4 [=] [%i]	FIN	**1.50**
9. Compute account balance for quarterly compounding.	[2nd] [FV]	FIN	**5978.09**
10. Calculate difference.	[+/−] [+] [RCL] [=]	FIN	**8.00**

In three years, you will earn $8 more with continuous compounding.

Reference:

Greynolds, Aronofsky, and Frame, *Financial Analysis Using Calculators: Time Value of Money*, pp. 173-182.

CHAPTER 3

Determining the Continuous Annual Interest Rate on an Annuity

Assume that you pay $6726 for an annuity that pays $100 at the *end* of each month for eight years. What is the annual interest rate compounded continuously? (*Note*: This is an ordinary annuity because payments occur at the end of each period.)

In annuity situations where the annual continuous rate is known, the formula for finding the equivalent discrete rate is

$$i = e^{r/f} - 1$$

where i is the equivalent annual discrete rate per payment period, r is the annual continuous rate, and f is the number of payments per year. To find the annual continuous rate, first solve for the discrete rate per payment period and then convert the result to the continuous rate with the formula

$$r = \ln(1 + i) \times f$$

where r and i are decimals.

Procedure	Press		Display
1. Clear calculator and mode registers; select two decimal places.	[ON/C] [2nd] [CMR] [FIX] 2		**0.00**
2. Select financial mode ("FIN" shows in the display).	[2nd] [Mode]	FIN	**0.00**
3. Enter number of payments.	8 [×] 12 [=] [N]	FIN	**96.00**
4. Enter amount of payment.	100 [PMT]	FIN	**100.00**
5. Enter amount of investment.	6726 [PV]	FIN	**6726.00**
6. Compute discrete interest rate per payment period.	[2nd] [%i]	FIN	**0.78**

Procedure	Press		Display
7. Convert discrete interest rate to equivalent continuous rate.*			
a. Convert percent to decimal.	[%]	FIN	**0.01**
b. Calculate continuous rate per payment period as a decimal.	[+] 1 [=] [2nd] [lnx]	FIN	**0.01**
c. Multiply by number of payments per year to calculate annual continuous rate.	[×] 12 [=]	FIN	**0.09**
d. Multiply by 100 to find rate as a percent.	[×] 100 [=]	FIN	**9.38**

The annual interest rate compounded continuously is 9.38%.

*See *Appendix A* for the formulas.

Reference:

Greynolds, Aronofsky, and Frame, *Financial Analysis Using Calculators: Time Value of Money*, pp. 182-187.

CHAPTER 3

Determining a Regular Deposit with Continuous Compounding to Have a Certain Amount in the Future

In five years, Sam wants to have $20,000 in his savings account. The annual interest rate is 6% compounded continuously. If Sam plans to make a deposit at the beginning of each month, how much should he deposit?

Procedure	Press		Display
1. Clear calculator and mode registers; select two decimal places.	[ON/C] [2nd] [CMR] [FIX] 2		0.00
2. Select financial mode ("FIN" shows in the display).	[2nd] [Mode]	FIN	0.00
3. Convert continuous interest rate to equivalent discrete rate.*			
a. Divide continuous rate by number of payments per year.	6 [÷] 12 [=] [%]	FIN	0.01
b. Calculate equivalent discrete rate.	[2nd] [e^x] [−] 1 [=]	FIN	0.01
c. Convert to percent and enter equivalent discrete rate per payment period.	[×] 100 [=] [%i]	FIN	0.50
4. Calculate and enter number of deposits.	5 [×] 12 [=] [N]	FIN	60.00
5. Enter desired balance.	20000 [FV]	FIN	20000.00
6. Calculate monthly deposit amount.	[DUE] [PMT]	FIN	285.12

Sam would need to deposit $285.12 at the beginning of each month.

*See *Appendix A* for the formulas.

Reference:

Greynolds, Aronofsky, and Frame, *Financial Analysis Using Calculators: Time Value of Money*, pp. 182-187.

Determining the Continuous Annual Interest Rate on an Investment

You have an opportunity to invest $10,000 today and receive $20,000 after ten years. What is the continuous annual interest rate on this investment?

Procedure	Press		Display
1. Clear calculator and mode registers; select two decimal places.	[ON/C] [2nd] [CMR] [FIX] 2		**0.00**
2. Select financial mode ("FIN" shows in the display).	[2nd] [Mode]	FIN	**0.00**
3. Enter number of years.	10 [N]	FIN	**10.00**
4. Enter amount of investment.	10000 [PV]	FIN	**10000.00**
5. Enter future amount.	20000 [FV]	FIN	**20000.00**
6. Compute discrete interest rate compounded at end of each year.	[2nd] [%i]	FIN	**7.18**
7. Convert discrete interest rate to equivalent continuous rate.*			
a. Convert percent to decimal.	[%]	FIN	**0.07**
b. Calculate continuous rate as a decimal.	[+] 1 [=] [2nd] [lnx]	FIN	**0.07**
c. Multiply by 100 to convert to percent.	[×] 100 [=]	FIN	**6.93**

You will earn a continuously compounded annual interest rate of 6.93%.

*See *Appendix A* for the formulas.

Reference:

Greynolds, Aronofsky, and Frame, *Financial Analysis Using Calculators*: *Time Value of Money*, pp. 173-182.

CHAPTER

4 DEPRECIATION

One of the necessary calculations required in the financial operations of almost every company, large or small, is the depreciation of various pieces of capital equipment. We'll review here the three major depreciation methods (straight-line, sum-of-the-years'-digits, and declining balance).

The *straight-line* method assumes that the amount of depreciation is the same each year. In the *sum-of-the-years'-digits* (SYD) method, the amount of depreciation decreases each year, as determined by the estimated life of the asset. With the *declining balance* method, the amount of depreciation is determined by multiplying the depreciable value of the equipment at the end of the preceding year by a constant percentage. (*Reference*: Kieso and Weygandt, *Intermediate Accounting*, pp. 487-490, 493-494.)

In this chapter, we discuss each of these three methods with an example of an asset purchased during a fiscal (financial) year. In this type of situation, the asset is depreciated for the remainder of the first year, and the depreciation expense is allocated between fiscal years. As a result, the amount of depreciation is recorded for one calendar year beyond the asset's life.

Assume that a pizza company begins its fiscal year January 1st and purchases an oven on April 1st. The oven costs $5,000 and has a five-year life with an anticipated salvage value of $750.

Straight-Line

COST = $5000 LIFE OF ASSET = 5 years
SALVAGE VALUE = $750 PURCHASE DATE = April 1

Procedure	Press	Display
1. Clear calculator and select two decimal places.	[ON/C] [STO] [FIX] 2	**0.00**
2. Calculate depreciable value (cost − salvage value).	5000 [−] 750 [=]	**4250.00**
3. Divide by life of asset to calculate annual depreciation.	[÷] 5 [=]	**850.00**
4. Calculate and store depreciation for year 1 (April 1 to Dec. 31 = 9 months or 9/12 years).	[×] 9 [÷] 12 [=] [STO]	**637.50**
5. Calculate depreciation for year 6 (Jan. 1 to March 31 = 3 months) and add to memory.	850 [×] 3 [÷] 12 [=] [SUM]	**212.50**
6. Calculate depreciation for years 2, 3, 4, and 5 (a total of four years) and add to memory.	850 [×] 4 [=] [SUM]	**3400.00**
7. Recall total accumulated depreciation. (This value should equal the depreciable value calculated in step 2.)	[RCL]	**4250.00**

See *Appendix A* for the formula.

Sum-of-the-Years'-Digits (SYD)

COST = $5000 LIFE OF ASSET = 5 years
SALVAGE VALUE = $750 PURCHASE DATE = April 1

NOTE: To calculate the sum-of-the-year's digits factor, follow this procedure (see step 2, below):

LIFE × (LIFE + 1) ÷ 2

Procedure	Press	Display
1. Clear calculator and select two decimal places.	[ON/C] [STO] [FIX] 2	**0.00**
2. Calculate and store sum of years.	5 [×] 6 [÷] 2 [=] [STO]	**15.00**
3. Calculate depreciable value (cost − salvage value).	5000 [−] 750 [=]	**4250.00**
4. Divide by sum of years and store.	[÷] [RCL] [=] [STO]	**283.33**
5. Calculate depreciation expense for whole year 1 (life of asset + 1 − year number) using value computed in step 4 as a constant.	5 [×] [K] [RCL] [=]	**1416.67**

Procedure	Press	Display
6. Compute depreciation for whole year 2.	4 [=]	**1133.33**
7. Compute depreciation for whole year 3.	3 [=]	**850.00**
8. Compute depreciation for whole year 4.	2 [=]	**566.67**
9. Compute depreciation for whole year 5.	1 [=]	**283.33**
10. Calculate depreciation expense for fiscal year 1.	9 [÷] 12 [×] 1416.67 [=]	**1062.50**
11. Calculate depreciation expense for fiscal year 2.		
a. Calculate depreciation for January 1 to March 31 of fiscal year 2 (3 ÷ 12 × year 1 depreciation).	3 [÷] 12 [×] 1416.67 [=] [STO]	**354.17**
b. Calculate depreciation for April 1 to December 31 of fiscal year 2 (9 ÷ 12 × year 2 depreciation).	9 [÷] 12 [×] 1133.33 [=]	**850.00**
c. Calculate total depreciation for year 2; (a + b).	[+] [RCL] [=]	**1204.17**

(continued on next page)

Procedure	Press	Display
13. Calculate depreciation expense for fiscal year 3.		
a. Calculate depreciation for January 1 to March 31 of fiscal year 3 (3 ÷ 12 × year 2 depreciation).	3 [÷] 12 [×] 1133.33 [=] [STO]	**283.33**
b. Calculate depreciation for April 1 to December 31 of fiscal year 3 (9 ÷ 12 × year 3 depreciation).	9 [÷] 12 [×] 850 [=]	**637.50**
c. Calculate total depreciation for year 3; (a + b).	[+] [RCL] [=]	**920.83**
14. Calculate depreciation expense for fiscal year 4.		
a. Calculate depreciation for January 1 to March 31 of fiscal year 4 (3 ÷ 12 × year 3 depreciation).	3 [÷] 12 [×] 850 [=] [STO]	**212.50**
b. Calculate depreciation for April 1 to December 31 of fiscal year 4 (9 ÷ 12 × year 4 depreciation).	9 [÷] 12 [×] 566.67 [=]	**425.00**
c. Calculate total depreciation for year 4; (a + b).	[+] [RCL] [=]	**637.50**

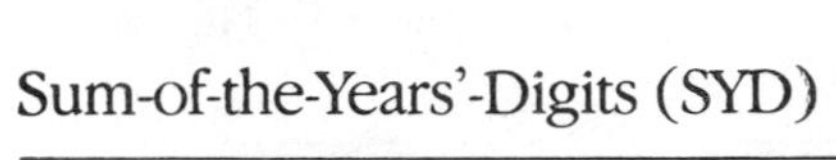

Sum-of-the-Years'-Digits (SYD)

Procedure	Press	Display
15. Calculate depreciation expense for fiscal year 5.		
a. Calculate depreciation for January 1 to March 31 of fiscal year 5 (3 ÷ 12 × year 4 depreciation).	3 [÷] 12 [×] 566.67 [=] [STO]	**141.67**
b. Calculate depreciation for April 1 to December 31 of fiscal year 5 (9 ÷ 12 × year 5 depreciation).	9 [÷] 12 [×] 283.33 [=]	**212.50**
c. Calculate total depreciation for year 5; (a + b).	[+] [RCL] [=]	**354.17**
16. Calculate depreciation for January 1 to March 31 of fiscal year 6 (3 ÷ 12 × year 5 depreciation).	3 [÷] 12 [×] 283.33 [=]	**70.83**

The depreciation expense is $1062.50 for fiscal year 1, $1204.17 for year 2, $920.83 for year 3, $637.50 for year 4, $354.17 for year 5, and $70.83 for year 6.

See *Appendix A* for the formulas.

Declining Balance

COST = $5000 LIFE OF ASSET = 5 years
SALVAGE VALUE = $750 PURCHASE DATE = April 1

For this example, use a 200% factor. Note also that the depreciation stops when the depreciable value equals the salvage value, while the SYD method continued until the sixth year.

Procedure	Press	Display
1. Clear calculator and select two decimal places.	[ON/C] [STO] [FIX] 2	**0.00**
2. Divide declining balance factor by asset life and store.	200 [÷] 5 [=] [STO]	**40.00**
3. Calculate first partial year depreciation.		
a. Multiply by cost to calculate depreciation for first calendar year.	[%] [×] 5000 [=]	**2000.00**
b. Compute partial year depreciation.	[×] 9 [÷] 12 [=]	**1500.00**
4. Calculate net depreciable value at start of second year.	[+/−] [+] 5000 [=]	**3500.00**

Procedure	Press	Display
5. Calculate depreciation expense for year 2.	[−] [RCL] [%]	**1400.00**
6. Calculate depreciable value at end of year 2.	[=]	**2100.00**
7. Calculate depreciation expense for year 3.	[−] [RCL] [%]	**840.00**
8. Calculate depreciable value at end of year 3.	[=]	**1260.00**
9. Calculate depreciation expense for year 4.	[−] [RCL] [%]	**504.00**
10. Calculate depreciable value at end of year 4.	[=]	**756.00**
11. Calculate depreciation expense for last year.	[−] 750 [=]	**6.00**

The depreciation stops in year 5 with a depreciation expense of $6.00 because in year 6 the depreciable value would be less than the $750 salvage value.

See *Appendix A* for the formula.

CHAPTER

5 REAL ESTATE

Real estate today is a dynamic field, with changes occurring almost daily. These changes are reflected in many aspects of financing, including mortgage packaging, computing income taxes, and determining rates of return. These and other factors influence the ultimate decision — whether to invest in a real estate package or not. Interested individuals run the gamut from the one-time investor, who wants to know how much to invest in a single family house, to the builder-developer, who is interested in tax benefits, depreciation allowances, and reduced taxable income.

In the past the mathematical and statistical applications required for making a decision were often tedious, time-consuming and prone to error. Not so anymore. Welcome to the world of calculator analysis for real estate! Your calculator brings you the means of calculating many of the ratios, rates of return, and other analytical techniques that can help you arrive at the best real estate decision. The range of the calculator's applications is limited only by your curiosity, imagination, and real estate knowledge.

The interest rates used in real estate calculations can be either the Annual Percent Interest Rate (APR) or the annual effective interest rate. The APR is converted to the interest rate per compounding period (APR ÷ number of compounding periods per year) for use in calculations. The effective rate is the rate at which interest is actually compounded for a year. In this chapter, the interest rates given are APR.

Comparing House Cost Per Square Foot

You are looking at two houses. House A has 2000 square feet of living space and costs $84,000. House B has 2300 square feet of living space and costs $92,000. Based on cost per square foot, which house is the best buy?

Procedure	Press	Display
1. Clear calculator and select floating decimal point.	[ON/C] [FIX] 8	**0**
2. Calculate cost per square foot of House A.	84000 [÷] 2000 [=]	**42**
3. Calculate cost per square foot of House B.	92000 [÷] 2300 [=]	**40**

House B costs $2 less per square foot than House A.

Calculation of Down Payment

You plan to sell your house for an appraised value of $33,000. You still owe $27,500 on the mortgage. If the buyer wants to assume your mortgage, what percentage down payment would be necessary?

Procedure	Press	Display
1. Clear calculator and select two decimal places.	[ON/C] [FIX] 2	**0.00**
2. Calculate amount of down payment.	33000 [−] 27500 [=]	**5500.00**
3. Calculate percentage of down payment.	[÷] 33000 [×] 100 [=]	**16.67**

The buyer would have to make a 16.67% down payment.

CHAPTER 5

Calculation of Agent's Commission

The total commission paid when selling a house is often 6% of the purchase price. The real estate firm gets half the total commission (3%) and the Listing Service gets the other half. Your agent earns half the commission collected by the real estate firm. How much would your agent earn for selling your $38,000 home; what would the Listing Service get?

Procedure	Press	Display
1. Clear calculator and select two decimal places.	[ON/C] [FIX] 2	**0.00**
2. Calculate total commission.	38000 [×] 6 [%] [=]	**2280.00**
3. Calculate amount of commission for real estate firm and Listing Service.	[÷] 2 [=]	**1140.00**
4. Calculate amount of agent's fee.	[÷] 2 [=]	**570.00**

The agent would earn $570, and the Listing Service would receive $1140.00.

Average Yearly Appreciation Rate

The house you bought for $37,075 in 1972 was appraised at $74,000 in 1980. What was the average annual appreciation rate? If the rate of appreciation remains the same, what will the house be worth in three years?

Procedure	Press		Display
1. Clear calculator and mode registers; select two decimal places.	[ON/C] [2nd] [CMR] [FIX] 2		**0.00**
2. Select financial mode ("FIN" shows in the display).	[2nd] [Mode]	FIN	**0.00**
3. Enter number of years.	8 [N]	FIN	**8.00**
4. Enter original cost.	37075 [PV]	FIN	**37075.00**
5. Enter current market value.	74000 [FV]	FIN	**74000.00**
6. Compute annual appreciation rate.	[2nd] [%i]	FIN	**9.02**
7. Enter new period.	3 [N]	FIN	**3.00**
8. Enter new present value (current appraisal value).	74000 [PV]	FIN	**74000.00**
9. Compute future value.	[2nd] [FV]	FIN	**95893.28**

The house is appreciating at an average annual rate of 9.02%. In three years, your house should be worth about $95,900 if the 9.02% appreciation rate continues.

CHAPTER 5

Actual Interest Rate Paid When Buyer Pays Points

Joe recently borrowed $76,000 for 30 years to purchase his dream home. His monthly payments of $774.44 are based on an annual interest rate of 11 7/8% compounded monthly. Joe had to pay 3 points to borrow the money. (A point is 1% of the loan amount.) Thus Joe only received $73,720 (97% of $76,000), but he must repay the full mortgage amount and pay interest on the full amount. What is the actual annual interest rate, compounded monthly, for Joe's mortgage?

Procedure	Press		Display
1. Clear calculator and mode registers; select two decimal places.	[ON/C] [2nd] [CMR] [FIX] 2		**0.00**
2. Select financial mode ("FIN" shows in the display).	[2nd] [Mode]	FIN	**0.00**
3. Calculate and enter number of payments.	30 [×] 12 [=] [N]	FIN	**360.00**
4. Enter monthly payment.	774.44 [PMT]	FIN	**774.44**
5. Subtract points from amount borrowed and enter as present value.	76000 [−] 3 [%] [=] [PV]	FIN	**73720.00**
6. Compute monthly interest rate.	[2nd] [%i]	FIN	**1.02**
7. Calculate annual interest rate.	[×] 12 [=]	FIN	**12.28**

Joe is actually paying 12.28% annual interest, compounded monthly.

Determining Selling Price of a House If Seller Pays Points

You originally paid $60,000 for your house and now want to sell it for a $25,000 profit. If the lending institution requires you to pay 5 points (5%), what is the selling price of the house?

Procedure	Press	Display
1. Clear calculator and select two decimal places.	[ON/C] [STO] [FIX] 2	**0.00**
2. Enter 1 (one), subtract points, and store result.	1 [−] 5 [%] [=] [STO]	**0.95**
3. Add original price and profit.	60000 [+] 25000 [=]	**85000.00**
4. Calculate selling price.	[÷] [RCL] [=]	**89473.68**

To make a $25,000 profit, you would need to sell your house for $89,473.68.

CHAPTER 5

Monthly Payment for Home Mortgage

You are buying a $57,500 house. You plan to make a $5800 down payment and finance the rest at 11.75% annual interest for 30 years. Excluding taxes and insurance, how much will your monthly payments be on the loan? If taxes and insurance will average 30% of your loan payment each month, how much will your total house payment be? (*Note:* Since payments occur at the end of each month, this is an ordinary annuity situation.)

Procedure	Press		Display
1. Clear calculator and mode registers; select two decimal places.	[ON/C] [2nd] [CMR] [FIX] 2		0.00
2. Select financial mode ("FIN" shows in the display).	[2nd] [Mode]	FIN	0.00
3. Calculate and enter number of payments.	30 [×] 12 [=] [N]	FIN	360.00
4. Calculate and enter monthly interest rate.	11.75 [÷] 12 [=] [%i]	FIN	0.98
5. Calculate and enter loan amount (cost of house − down payment).	57500 [−] 5800 [=] [PV]	FIN	51700.00
6. Compute monthly payment.	[2nd] [PMT]	FIN	**521.86**
7. Add estimated taxes and insurance to calculate total monthly house payment.	[+] 30 [%] [=]	FIN	**678.42**

The monthly payments on the loan are $521.86, and the total monthly house payments are $678.42.

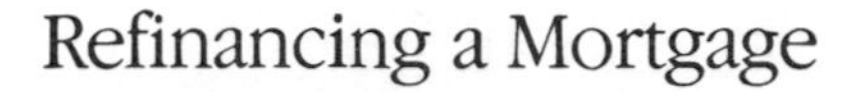

Refinancing a Mortgage

Assume that 210 payments of $813.69 each remain on your current mortgage, and the unpaid balance is $65,425.33. The current annual interest rate is 13.5% compounded monthly, and you can refinance the mortgage at a rate of 10% compounded monthly. How much will your monthly payment be if you refinance the mortgage over the remaining 210 payments?

Procedure	Press		Display
1. Clear calculator and mode registers; select two decimal places.	[ON/C] [2nd] [CMR] [FIX] 2		**0.00**
2. Select financial mode ("FIN" shows in the display).	[2nd] [Mode]	FIN	**0.00**
3. Enter number of monthly payments.	210 [N]	FIN	**210.00**
4. Calculate and enter new monthly interest rate.	10 [÷] 12 [=] [%i]	FIN	**0.83**
5. Enter amount to be refinanced.	65425.33 [PV]	FIN	**65425.33**
6. Compute amount of new payment.	[2nd] [PMT]	FIN	**660.89**

Your new monthly payment will be $660.89.

Loan Amount a Buyer Can Afford

A loan company will usually finance a house if the potential monthly payment does not exceed 25% of a buyer's gross income. Assume you have a gross monthly income of $2700. What price house can you afford to finance at a 12% annual interest rate for 30 years with 15% down? Monthly taxes and insurance will be 30% of the loan payment.

Procedure	Press		Display
1. Clear calculator and mode registers; select two decimal places.	[ON/C] [STO] [2nd] [CMR] [FIX] 2		0.00
2. Select financial mode ("FIN" shows in the display).	[2nd] [Mode]	FIN	0.00
3. Calculate and enter number of monthly payments.	30 [×] 12 [=] [N]	FIN	360.00
4. Calculate and enter monthly interest rate.	12 [÷] 12 [=] [%i]	FIN	1.00
5. Calculate and store maximum allowable monthly payment (including taxes and insurance).	2700 [×] 25 [%] [=] [STO]	FIN	675.00
6. Calculate and enter maximum allowable loan payment.	1 [+] 30 [%] [=] [1/x] [×] [RCL] [=] [PMT]	FIN	519.23
7. Compute and store maximum allowable loan amount.	[2nd] [PV] [STO]	FIN	50478.75
8. Calculate affordable house price.	1 [−] 15 [%] [=] [1/x] [×] [RCL] [=]	FIN	59386.76
9. Calculate down payment.	[−] [RCL] [=]	FIN	8908.01

You can afford to finance a $59,386 house, and your down payment will be $8,908.

Time Required to Pay Off Mortgage

The monthly payments for the mortgage on your house are $384.46 (excluding taxes and insurance). The annual interest rate is 8.5% compounded monthly. In the past you have made extra principal payments, and your current loan balance is $44,612.57. How many payments remain if you make the regular $384.46 payment each month? What happens if you pay $400 each month?

Procedure	Press		Display
1. Clear calculator and mode registers; select two decimal places.	[ON/C] [STO] [2nd] [CMR] [FIX] 2		**0.00**
2. Select financial mode ("FIN" shows in the display).	[2nd] [Mode]	FIN	**0.00**
3. Calculate and enter interest rate per payment period.	8.5 [÷] 12 [=] [%i]	FIN	**0.71**
4. Enter required monthly payment.	384.46 [PMT]	FIN	**384.46**
5. Enter mortgage balance.	44612.57 [PV]	FIN	**44612.57**
6. Compute and store number of remaining payments.	[2nd] [N] [STO]	FIN	**244.49**
7. Enter increased payment.	400 [PMT]	FIN	**400.00**
8. Compute number of payments.	[2nd] [N]	FIN	**221.12**
9. Calculate difference.	[+/−] [+] [RCL] [=]	FIN	**23.37**

By increasing the amount of your monthly payments to $400, you can reduce the term of the loan by approximately 23 payments or almost two years.

Amount to Pay for a Mortgage to Achieve a Specified Yield

Joe Brown loaned Fred Smith $10,000 at 8.5% annual interest for ten years. Fred's payments to Joe are $123.99 per month. Two years later (right after the 24th payment), Joe has an immediate need for cash; and he asks you to buy the remaining loan payments from him. You earn a 9% annual rate, compounded monthly, from your other investments, so you are only willing to buy the mortgage if you can realize a 9% rate of return. What would you offer to pay Joe Brown for the balance of the loan?

Procedure	Press		Display
1. Clear calculator and mode registers; select two decimal places.	[ON/C] [2nd] [CMR] [FIX] 2		0.00
2. Select financial mode ("FIN" shows in the display).	[2nd] [Mode]	FIN	0.00
3. Calculate and enter number of periods left in loan.	10 [×] 12 [−] 24 [=] [N]	FIN	96.00
4. Calculate and enter monthly interest rate.	9 [÷] 12 [=] [%i]	FIN	0.75
5. Enter monthly payment.	123.99 [PMT]	FIN	123.99
6. Compute present value of future payments.	[2nd] [PV]	FIN	**8463.36**

Any offer under $8463 would represent a profitable investment returning at least 9% annually.

How Much of a Given Payment on a Home Is Principal, and How Much Is Interest?

Assume that you have made 85 payments on your home. Your original loan was for $32,000 with an 8.5% interest rate, and your payments (less taxes and insurance) are $250 per month. You would like to know how much of your next two loan payments will be interest and how much will be added to your equity (the amount of your loan that is paid off).

Procedure	Press		Display
1. Clear calculator and mode registers; select two decimal places.	ON/C 2nd CMR FIX 2		**0.00**
2. Select financial mode ("FIN" shows in the display).	2nd Mode	FIN	**0.00**
3. Calculate and enter monthly interest rate.	8.5 ÷ 12 = %i	FIN	**0.71**
4. Enter monthly payment.	250 PMT	FIN	**250.00**
5. Enter original loan amount.	32000 PV	FIN	**32000.00**
6. Compute original number of payments.	2nd N	FIN	**336.00**
7. Enter number of next payment and calculate amount that applies to principal.	86 2nd P/I	FIN	**42.51**
8. Display interest amount in 86th payment.	x:y	FIN	**207.49**
9. Repeat steps 7 and 8 for payment number 87.	87 2nd P/I	FIN	**42.82**
	x:y	FIN	**207.18**

For payment number 86, the principal will be $42.51 and the interest will be $207.49. For number 87, the principal will be $42.82 and the interest will be $207.18.

CHAPTER 5 Balance Owed, Principal and Interest Paid at the End of a Specified Time on a Mortgage

You borrowed $32,000 to buy your house and have lived in it for nine years. Your monthly loan payments (not including taxes and insurance) are $299.72, and your mortgage carries 8.5% annual interest, compounded monthly. How much interest have you paid? How much of the loan have you paid off? How much interest did you pay during the ninth year?

Procedure	Press		Display
1. Clear calculator and mode registers; select two decimal places.	[ON/C] [STO] [2nd] [CMR] [FIX] 2		**0.00**
2. Select financial mode ("FIN" shows in the display).	[2nd] [Mode]	FIN	**0.00**
3. Calculate and enter interest rate per payment period.	8.5 [÷] 12 [=] [%i]	FIN	**0.71**
4. Enter monthly payment.	299.72 [PMT]	FIN	**299.72**
5. Enter original loan amount.	32000 [PV]	FIN	**32000.00**
6. Solve for total number of payments.	[2nd] [N]	FIN	**200.00**

Balance Owed, Principal and Interest Paid at the End of a Specified Time on a Mortgage

Procedure	Press		Display
7. Compute and store interest paid over time period (9 years).	12 [×] 9 [=]	FIN	**108.00**
	[2nd] [Acc/Bal] [STO]	FIN	**20579.39**
8. Display remaining balance on mortgage.	[x:y]	FIN	**20209.63**
9. Subtract remaining balance from original loan amount to calculate amount of principal paid.	[+/−] [+] 32000 [=]	FIN	**11790.37**
10. Compute interest paid for eight years.	12 [×] 8 [=]	FIN	**96.00**
	[2nd] [Acc/Bal]	FIN	**18777.86**
11. Subtract interest paid for eight years from interest paid for nine years (step 7) to calculate interest paid during ninth year.	[+/−] [+] [RCL] [=]	FIN	**1801.54**

Assuming that all payments made were $299.72, you have paid $20,579.39 in interest and $11,790.37 in principal on the loan. The interest paid during the ninth year was $1,801.54.

Preparing a Mortgage Amortization Schedule

You have just sold a house, and the buyer wants an amortization schedule for the four months remaining in that year. The mortgage amount is $68,500 for 30 years, and the annual interest rate is 13.25% compounded monthly. The monthly payment is $771.15.

Procedure	Press		Display
1. Clear calculator and mode registers; select two decimal places.	[ON/C] [2nd] [CMR] [FIX] 2		**0.00**
2. Select financial mode ("FIN" shows in the display).	[2nd] [Mode]	FIN	**0.00**
3. Calculate and enter monthly interest rate.	13.25 [÷] 12 [=] [%i]	FIN	**1.10**
4. Enter monthly payment.	771.15 [PMT]	FIN	**771.15**
5. Enter loan amount.	68500 [PV]	FIN	**68500.00**
6. Compute total number of payments.	[2nd] [N]	FIN	**360.03**
7. Compute amount of principal for first payment.	1 [2nd] [P/I]	FIN	**14.80**
8. Display amount of interest for first payment.	[x:y]	FIN	**756.35**

Procedure	Press		Display
9. Compute loan balance after first payment.	1 [2nd] [Acc/Bal] [x:y]	FIN	**68485.20**
10. Repeat steps 7, 8, and 9 for payments 2, 3, and 4.			
a. Payment 2:			
Principal	2 [2nd] [P/I]	FIN	**14.96**
Interest	[x:y]	FIN	**756.19**
Balance	2 [2nd] [Acc/Bal] [x:y]	FIN	**68470.25**
b. Payment 3:			
Principal	3 [2nd] [P/I]	FIN	**15.12**
Interest	[x:y]	FIN	**756.03**
Balance	3 [2nd] [Acc/Bal] [x:y]	FIN	**68455.12**
c. Payment 4:			
Principal	4 [2nd] [P/I]	FIN	**15.29**
Interest	[x:y]	FIN	**755.86**
Balance	4 [2nd] [Acc/Bal] [x:y]	FIN	**68439.83**

NOTE: Your calculator does *not* round to two decimal places when calculating principal, interest, or remaining balance. However, many lending institutions round to the nearest cent. For this reason, you may occasionally find a small difference between your calculations and their amortization schedules.

CHAPTER 5

Determining Original Cost and Appreciation of Existing Property

Your friend has a five-year-old house that has been appraised at $48,000. He has an 8.5% 30-year loan and an unpaid balance of $26,834. Five years ago, 8.5% 30-year loans required a 20% down payment. You want to know two things: one, what was the original price of the house and, two, if he sells the house for $48,000, what was his average yearly appreciation rate?

Procedure	Press		Display
1. Clear calculator and mode registers; select two decimal places.	[ON/C] [STO] [2nd] [CMR] [FIX] 2		**0.00**
2. Select financial mode ("FIN" shows in the display).	[2nd] [Mode]	FIN	**0.00**
3. Calculate and enter number of remaining payments.	30 [−] 5 [×] 12 [=] [N]	FIN	**300.00**
4. Calculate and enter monthly interest rate.	8.5 [÷] 12 [=] [%i]	FIN	**0.71**
5. Enter unpaid balance.	26834 [PV]	FIN	**26834.00**
6. Compute monthly loan payment.	[2nd] [PMT]	FIN	**216.07**
7. Calculate and enter original number of payment periods.	30 [×] 12 [=] [N]	FIN	**360.00**
8. Compute and store original loan amount.	[2nd] [PV] [STO]	FIN	**28101.29**
9. Calculate original price of home and enter as present value.	1 [−] 20 [%] [=] [1/x] [×] [RCL] [=] [PV]	FIN	**35126.62**
10. Compute annual appreciation rate.	5 [N]	FIN	**5.00**
	0 [PMT]	FIN	**0.00**
	48000 [FV]	FIN	**48000.00**
	[2nd] [%i]	FIN	**6.44**

The original cost of the house was $35,126.62, and the average yearly appreciation rate has been 6.44%.

Determining the Price of a Mortgage with a Balloon Payment Necessary to Receive a Specified Yield

You are looking for an investment that will pay 15% annual interest, compounded monthly, on your money. A friend offers to sell you a ten-year mortgage. The monthly payments are $141.92 with a final balloon payment of $3000. What would you pay for the mortgage to earn 15% annual interest, compounded monthly?

The total price of the mortgage is the sum of the present value of the balloon payment (steps 3 through 6) and the present value of the monthly loan payments (steps 7 through 9).

Procedure	Press		Display
1. Clear calculator and mode registers; select two decimal places.	[ON/C] [STO] [2nd] [CMR] [FIX] 2		**0.00**
2. Select financial mode ("FIN" shows in the display).	[2nd] [Mode]	FIN	**0.00**
3. Calculate and enter number of periods.	10 [×] 12 [=] [N]	FIN	**120.00**
4. Calculate and enter monthly interest rate.	15 [÷] 12 [=] [%i]	FIN	**1.25**
5. Enter amount of balloon payment.	3000 [FV]	FIN	**3000.00**
6. Compute and store present value of balloon payment.	[2nd] [PV] [STO]	FIN	**675.64**
7. Calculate and enter number of payments (excluding balloon payment).	10 [×] 12 [−] 1 [=] [N]	FIN	**119.00**
8. Enter monthly payment.	141.92 [PMT]	FIN	**141.92**
9. Compute present value of monthly payments.	[2nd] [PV]	FIN	**8764.64**
10. Add present value of balloon payment to calculate total price.	[+] [RCL] [=]	FIN	**9440.29**

If your friend will sell you the mortgage for about $9400, you will achieve your desired return.

CHAPTER

5 Determining the Monthly Payment for a Mortgage with a Balloon Payment

You are considering buying a $15,000 lake house, but you want the payments to be as small as possible. You know that you'll receive $3000 from an insurance policy in 14 years and would like that money to be a balloon payment on the lake house mortgage (and also serve as the last payment). If the 14-year mortgage (including the balloon payment) is set at 9.25% annual interest, compounded monthly, what would your monthly payment be?

A balloon payment is one which is made at the end of a series of regular payments. The balloon may be larger or smaller than the regular payment and can be used to pay off a loan before its normal duration is complete.

The problem can be solved in the following manner:

1. Calculate the present value of the balloon payment (steps 3 through 6).
2. Determine the loan amount (step 7).
3. Compute the monthly payment amount needed to pay off the loan (steps 8 and 9).

Procedure	Press		Display
1. Clear calculator and mode registers; select two decimal places.	[ON/C] [2nd] [CMR] [FIX] 2		0.00
2. Select financial mode ("FIN" shows in the display).	[2nd] [Mode]	FIN	0.00

Determining the Monthly Payment for a Mortgage with a Balloon Payment

Procedure	Press		Display
3. Calculate and enter number of payments.	14 [×] 12 [=] [N]	FIN	**168.00**
4. Calculate and enter monthly interest rate.	9.25 [÷] 12 [=] [%i]	FIN	**0.77**
5. Enter balloon payment.	3000 [FV]	FIN	**3000.00**
6. Compute present value of balloon payment.	[2nd] [PV]	FIN	**825.78**
7. Subtract balloon from cost of house and enter as present value of loan.	[+/-] [+] 15000 [=] [PV]	FIN	**14174.22**
8. Calculate and enter number of regular payments (balloon is last payment).	14 [×] 12 [-] 1 [=] [N]	FIN	**167.00**
9. Compute monthly payment.	[2nd] [PMT]	FIN	**151.20**

Your monthly payment on the lake house would be $151.20.

Reference:

Greynolds, Aronofsky, and Frame, *Financial Analysis Using Calculators: Time Value of Money,* Chapter 8.

CHAPTER 5

Loan Amount a Buyer Can Afford on a Mortgage with a Balloon Payment

You are considering a 20-year mortgage with an annual interest rate of 12.75% compounded monthly. The final payment will be a balloon payment of $25,000 and is to be included in the mortgage. If you can pay $850 per month for principal and interest, how much can you borrow?

In general, the problem can be solved as follows:

1. Find the present value of the balloon payment (steps 3 through 6).
2. Find the present value of the monthly payments (steps 7 through 9).
3. Add the present values of the balloon and monthly payments to calculate total mortgage amount (step 10).

Procedure	Press		Display
1. Clear calculator and mode registers; select two decimal places.	[ON/C] [STO] [2nd] [CMR] [FIX] 2		**0.00**
2. Select financial mode ("FIN" shows in the display).	[2nd] [Mode]	FIN	**0.00**
3. Calculate and enter number of periods.	20 [×] 12 [=] [N]	FIN	**240.00**
4. Calculate and enter monthly interest rate.	12.75 [÷] 12 [=] [%i]	FIN	**1.06**
5. Enter balloon payment.	25000 [FV]	FIN	**25000.00**

Loan Amount a Buyer Can Afford on a Mortgage with a Balloon Payment

Procedure	Press		Display
6. Compute and store present value of balloon payment.	[2nd] [PV] [STO]	FIN	**1978.48**
7. Calculate number of regular payments (excluding balloon).	20 [×] 12 [−] 1 [=] [N]	FIN	**239.00**
8. Enter amount of payment.	850 [PMT]	FIN	**850.00**
9. Compute present value of regular payments.	[2nd] [PV]	FIN	**73601.60**
10. Add present value of balloon payment to present value of regular payments to calculate total amount of mortgage.	[+] [RCL] [=]	FIN	**75580.08**

You can borrow $75,580.08. Notice that the $25,000 balloon payment only increased the amount you can borrow by $1,978.48.

CHAPTER 5 Calculating the Balloon Payment Needed to Pay Off a Loan

It is sometimes advantageous to pay off a loan with a balloon payment before the scheduled termination of the mortgage.

The following procedure easily calculates the size of balloon payment needed for early payoff of a mortgage, assuming that the scheduled payment has been made each month.

Consider a mortgage balance of $250,000 that is to terminate in 25 years. If the annual interest rate is 10 1/2%, compounded monthly, what balloon payment must be made in 15 years to pay off the loan?

The balloon payment, in this case, is the balance remaining on the mortgage after 15 years.

Procedure	Press		Display
1. Clear calculator and mode registers; select two decimal places.	[ON/C] [2nd] [CMR] [FIX] 2		**0.00**
2. Select financial mode ("FIN" shows in the display).	[2nd] [Mode]	FIN	**0.00**
3. Calculate and enter number of periods for original mortgage.	25 [×] 12 [=] [N]	FIN	**300.00**
4. Calculate and enter monthly interest rate.	10.5 [÷] 12 [=] [%i]	FIN	**0.88**
5. Enter amount of mortgage.	250000 [PV]	FIN	**250000.00**
6. Compute monthly payment.	[2nd] [PMT]	FIN	**2360.45**

Calculating the Balloon Payment Needed to Pay Off a Loan

Procedure	Press		Display
7. Enter amount of payment rounded to the nearest cent.*	2360.45 [PMT]	FIN	**2360.45**
8. Compute number of periods.	[2nd] [N]	FIN	**300.00**
9. Calculate number of payments you will have made at end of 15th year.	15 [×] 12 [=]	FIN	**180.00**
10. Calculate balloon payment.	[2nd] [Acc/Bal] [x:y]	FIN	**174934.55**

A balloon payment of $174,934.55 would be required to pay off the loan.

*Although the display in step 6 shows the payment amount rounded to two decimal places, the calculator would use all internal digits (up to 11) for subsequent calculations. For proper results, the payment amount must be rounded to two decimal places and then entered in step 7 because the bank or lending institution would use the rounded value, and not the calculator's internal value, in its calculations.

Finding the Interest Rate on a Mortgage with a Balloon Payment When the Buyer Pays Points

Assume that you want to borrow $80,000 for 15 years with a monthly payment of $853.81 and a final balloon payment of $70,124.92 (including the last monthly payment). The stated annual interest rate is 12.5% compounded monthly. However, you must pay 4 points to obtain the loan. In other words you are actually borrowing $76,800 (96% of $80,000) and repaying $80,000. What is the actual annual interest rate, compounded monthly, that you will pay for this mortgage?

Since the annuity equation cannot directly solve for the interest rate, the solution must be found through a repetitive, trial-and-error process known as an iteration. See steps 4 through 9.

Procedure	Press		Display
1. Clear calculator and mode registers; select three decimal places.	[ON/C] [STO] [2nd] [CMR] [FIX] 3		**0.000**
2. Select financial mode ("FIN" shows in the display).	[2nd] [Mode]	FIN	**0.000**
3. Calculate and enter number of periods.	15 [×] 12 [=] [N]	FIN	**180.000**
4. Calculate and store actual amount borrowed (loan amount − points).	80000 [−] 4 [%] [=] [STO]	FIN	**76800.000**
5. Calculate and enter future value (balloon amount − payment amount − actual loan amount ÷ actual loan amount × 100).	70124.92 [−] 853.81 [−] [RCL] [÷] [RCL] [×] 100 [=] [FV]	FIN	**-9.803**

Finding the Interest Rate on a Mortgage with a Balloon Payment When the Buyer Pays Points

Procedure	Press		Display
6. Calculate and store (payment amount ÷ actual loan amount × 100).	853.81 [÷] [RCL] [×] 100 [=] [STO]	FIN	**1.112**
7. Enter first estimate for %i. (Use the value calculated in step 6 or your own estimate.)	[%i]	FIN	**1.112**
8. Calculate second estimate for %i.	[2nd] [PMT] [+] [RCL] [=] [%i]	FIN	**1.094**
9. Calculate third estimate for %i.*	[2nd] [PMT] [+] [RCL] [=] [%i]	FIN	**1.094**
10. Multiply by number of periods per year to calculate annual interest rate.	[×] 12 [=]	FIN	**13.130**

The actual annual interest rate for this mortgage would be 13.13%.

* To find the interest rate with this procedure, repeat the key sequence for estimating the interest rate (steps 8 and 9) until the displayed answer equals the previous answer or until the answer reaches your desired level of accuracy. Notice that, in this case, the third estimate equals the second estimate so the iteration is complete in step 9. You might want to display more decimal places to increase the level of accuracy.

Home Improvement Loan (Long Term Versus Second Mortgages)

You have decided to buy a $64,500 house and would also like to make some improvements. You can finance the house for 30 years at an 11.25% annual interest rate, compounded monthly, with 10% down. You need $5,000 for improvements which you could borrow from another source. The improvement loan would be at 14% annual interest, compounded monthly, for two years. What would your monthly loan payment be for the two loans (during the first two years)? What would your monthly loan payment be if the improvement loan were included in the original house loan (added to the purchase price of the house)?

A. Calculate the total monthly payment when the home and improvement loans are financed separately.

Procedure	Press		Display
1. Clear calculator and mode registers; select two decimal places.	[ON/C] [STO] [2nd] [CMR] [FIX] 2		**0.00**
2. Select financial mode ("FIN" shows in the display).	[2nd] [Mode]	FIN	**0.00**
3. Calculate and enter number of periods in home loan.	30 [×] 12 [=] [N]	FIN	**360.00**
4. Calculate and enter monthly interest rate for home loan.	11.25 [÷] 12 [=] [%i]	FIN	**0.94**
5. Calculate amount of home loan after down payment and enter as present value.	64500 [−] 10 [%] [=] [PV]	FIN	**58050.00**
6. Compute and store payment for home loan.	[2nd] [PMT] [STO]	FIN	**563.82**
7. Calculate and enter number of periods in home improvement loan.	2 [×] 12 [=] [N]	FIN	**24.00**

Home Improvement Loan (Long Term Versus Second Mortgages)

	Procedure	Press		Display
8.	Calculate and enter monthly interest rate on home improvement loan.	14 [÷] 12 [=] [%i]	FIN	**1.17**
9.	Enter home improvement amount.	5000 [PV]	FIN	**5000.00**
10.	Compute monthly payment for home improvement loan.	[2nd] [PMT]	FIN	**240.06**
11.	**Add home loan payment to calculate total payment for both loans if financed separately.**	[+] [RCL] [=]	FIN	**803.88**

B. Calculate the total monthly payment for financing both loans for 30 years.

	Procedure	Press		Display
1.	Calculate and enter total number of payments.	30 [×] 12 [=] [N]	FIN	**360.00**
2.	Calculate and enter monthly interest rate.	11.25 [÷] 12 [=] [%i]	FIN	**0.94**
3.	Calculate total amount for home and improvement loan.	64500 [+] 5000 [=]	FIN	**69500.00**
4.	Subtract down payment and enter result as present value.	[−] 10 [%] [=] [PV]	FIN	**62550.00**
5.	**Compute total monthly payment.**	[2nd] [PMT]	FIN	**607.52**

The combined loan payments would be $803.88 for the first two years and $563.82 for the remaining 28 years. If the improvement loan could be included in the purchase price, the monthly payments would be $607.52 for 30 years.

CHAPTER 5 Six Functions of $1

Real estate practitioners often work with a set of tables, called the "Six Functions of $1," which usually have six columns labeled as follows:

- Amount of $1 at Compound Interest (Column 1)
- Accumulation of $1 Per Period (Column 2)
- Sinking Fund Factor (Column 3)
- Present Value of $1 or Reversion of $1, Compound Interest (Column 4)
- Present Value of an Ordinary Annuity at $1 Per Period (Column 5)
- Installment to Amortize $1 (Column 6)

With your calculator you can determine any of these six values without referring to the tables. The interest rates on the tables are often given in annual amounts with the number of annual compounding or payment periods specified. To calculate the values for Columns 1 and 4, enter the number of compounding periods for [N] and the interest rate per compounding period for [%i], and then calculate the future value of $1 and the reciprocal of the future value. (When you are solving for either of these values, the payment must be zero.) To determine the values in the other four columns, enter the number of payments for [N] and the interest rate per payment period for [%i] and calculate the appropriate value as shown in the following examples.

If any table value is known, enter all of the known values and solve for the unknown value, such as the number of compounding periods, the number of payments, or the interest rate.

Reference:

Hoagland, Stone, and Brueggeman, *Real Estate Finance,* Chapter 8.

Solving for the Column 1 and Column 4 Values

For an annual interest rate of 12.5% compounded monthly and with a 200 month period, compute the amount of $1 at compound interest (Column 1) and the present value of $1 (Column 4).

Procedure	Press		Display
1. Clear calculator and mode registers; select floating decimal point.	[ON/C] [2nd] [CMR] [FIX] 8		**0**
2. Select financial mode ("FIN" shows in the display).	[2nd] [Mode]	FIN	**0**
3. Enter number of compounding periods.	200 [N]	FIN	**200**
4. Calculate and enter interest rate per compounding period.	12.5 [÷] 12 [=] [%i]	FIN	**1.0416667**
5. Enter 1 for present value.	1 [PV]	FIN	**1**
6. Compute amount of $1 at compound interest (Column 1).	[2nd] [FV]	FIN	**7.9451163**
7. Calculate reciprocal of displayed value to find present value of $1 (Column 4).	[1/x]	FIN	**0.1258635**

The Column 1 value is 7.9451163, and the Column 4 value is 0.1258635.

Solving for the Column 2 and Column 3 Values

If the annual interest rate is 11.5% compounded monthly with 360 payments, find the accumulation of $1 per period (Column 2) and the sinking fund factor (Column 3).

Procedure	Press		Display
1. Clear calculator and mode registers; select floating decimal point.	[ON/C] [2nd] [CMR] [FIX] 8		**0**
2. Select financial mode ("FIN" shows in the display).	[2nd] [Mode]	FIN	**0**
3. Enter number of monthly payments.	360 [N]	FIN	**360**
4. Calculate and enter periodic interest rate.	11.5 [÷] 12 [=] [%i]	FIN	**0.9583333**
5. Enter 1 for payment.	1 [PMT]	FIN	**1**
6. Compute accumulation of $1 per period (Column 2).	[2nd] [FV]	FIN	**3129.0969**
7. Calculate reciprocal of displayed value to find sinking fund factor (Column 3).	[1/x]	FIN	**0.0003196**
8. Display more digits to right of decimal point.	[×] 10000 [=]	FIN	**3.1958103**

The Column 2 value is 3129.0969, and the Column 3 value is .00031958103.

Solving for the Column 5 and Column 6 Values

Using an annual interest rate of 10.75% compounded monthly and 240 monthly payments, find the present value of an ordinary annuity at $1 per period (Column 5) and the installment to amortize $1 (Column 6).

Procedure	Press		Display
1. Clear calculator and mode registers; select floating decimal point.	[ON/C] [2nd] [CMR] [FIX] 8		**0**
2. Select financial mode ("FIN" shows in the display).	[2nd] [Mode]	FIN	**0**
3. Enter number of monthly payments.	240 [N]	FIN	**240**
4. Calculate and enter periodic interest rate.	10.75 [÷] 12 [=] [%i]	FIN	**0.8958333**
5. Enter 1 for payment.	1 [PMT]	FIN	**1**
6. Compute present value of an ordinary annuity at $1 per period (Column 5).	[2nd] [PV]	FIN	**98.499949**
7. Calculate reciprocal of displayed value to find installment to amortize $1 (Column 6).	[1/x]	FIN	**0.0101523**
8. Multiply by number of periods per year to calculate annual constant.	[×] 12 [=]	FIN	**0.1218275**

The Column 5 value is 98.499949, and the Column 6 value is 0.0101523.

CHAPTER 5

Finding the Present Value of Income-Producing Property

Assume that a piece of property has 20 years remaining on a $22,000 per year lease, with payments made at the end of each year. The reversion value (FV) of the property is forecast to be $100,000. The applicable discount rate is 11% (interest rate). What should you expect to pay for the land today to meet the specified reversion value and discount rate?

This is a method used by appraisal people when they forecast a constant income stream (ordinary annuity) and a reversion value (the value of the property at the end of the time period). It is natural to presuppose a "stabilized" level stream for discounting to the present value. The procedure is:

1. Find the present value of the lease payments (steps 3 through 6).
2. Calculate the present value of the reversion (future) value (steps 7 through 9).
3. Add the above values to find the total present value of the property (step 10).

Procedure	Press		Display
1. Clear calculator and mode registers; select two decimal places.	[ON/C] [STO] [2nd] [CMR] [FIX] 2		0.00
2. Select financial mode ("FIN" shows in the display).	[2nd] [Mode]	FIN	0.00

Finding the Present Value of Income-Producing Property

	Procedure	Press		Display
3.	Enter number of years remaining on lease.	20 [N]	FIN	**20.00**
4.	Enter annual interest rate.	11 [%i]	FIN	**11.00**
5.	Enter annual payment.	22000 [PMT]	FIN	**22000.00**
6.	Compute and store present value of income stream.	[2nd] [PV] [STO]	FIN	**175193.22**
7.	Remove annual lease payment.	0 [PMT]	FIN	**0.00**
8.	Enter reversion value.	100000 [FV]	FIN	**100000.00**
9.	Compute present value of reversion value.	[2nd] [PV]	FIN	**12403.39**
10.	**Add to present value of lease payments to calculate present value of property.**	[+] [RCL] [=]	FIN	**187596.61**

You should expect to pay $187,597 for the land.

CHAPTER 5

Determining Reversion Value for Specified Yield

A lease that expires in 22 years requires a $15,500 monthly rental, payable in advance. As holder of this lease, you are negotiating with a prospective client who is considering offering $1,500,000 for the property holding. He wants to know what reversion value at the end of the 22-year lease period is necessary to realize a yield of 12%. He says that his real estate people quoted him a reversion value of $850,000. Do you agree or disagree?

In this instance, the reversion value of the property is the difference between the future value of the monthly rentals (steps 3 through 6) and the future value of the offered price (steps 7 through 9).

Procedure	Press		Display
1. Clear calculator and mode registers; select two decimal places.	[ON/C] [STO] [2nd] [CMR] [FIX] 2		**0.00**
2. Select financial mode ("FIN" shows in the display).	[2nd] [Mode]	FIN	**0.00**
3. Calculate and enter number of payments.	22 [×] 12 [=] [N]	FIN	**264.00**
4. Calculate and enter monthly interest rate.	12 [÷] 12 [=] [%i]	FIN	**1.00**
5. Enter rental payment.	15500 [PMT]	FIN	**15500.00**
6. Compute and store future value of rent payments.	[DUE] [FV] [STO]	FIN	**20086387**
7. Enter lease sale price.	1500000 [PV]	FIN	**1500000.0**
8. Enter 0 (zero) for payment.	0 [PMT]	FIN	**0.00**
9. Compute future value of lease sale price.	[2nd] [FV]	FIN	**20745979**
10. Calculate difference.	[−] [RCL] [=]	FIN	**659592.23**

The investor's advisors suggested a reversion value of $850,000, but your calculations indicate that the value of the property can drop to $660,000 at the end of 22 years and the investor will still receive his 12% return.

Buying Rental Property

One quick method that can be used to determine whether or not to buy a piece of rental property is to assume that you will buy only if the rent income from the property covers the taxes, maintenance, insurance, and loan payment for the value of the property. Assume that a house rents for $210 a month. You estimate that taxes, insurance, and maintenance will run $75 each month. If you can get a 25 year loan for the full cost of the house at 12.75% annual interest, compounded monthly, how much can you afford to pay for the house?

Procedure	Press		Display
1. Clear calculator and mode registers; select two decimal places.	[ON/C] [2nd] [CMR] [FIX] 2		**0.00**
2. Select financial mode ("FIN" shows in the display).	[2nd] [Mode]	FIN	**0.00**
3. Calculate and enter number of payments.	25 [×] 12 [=] [N]	FIN	**300.00**
4. Calculate and enter periodic interest rate (monthly).	12.75 [÷] 12 [=] [%i]	FIN	**1.06**
5. Calculate and enter amount of rent applicable to loan payment.	210 [−] 75 [=] [PMT]	FIN	**135.00**
6. Compute loan amount necessary to fulfill your specifications.	[2nd] [PV]	FIN	**12172.56**

A $12,173 house would be within your purchase limit.

CHAPTER 5

Investing in a Rental Property

For investment purposes, you're considering buying a house that is presently rented for $375 per month (payable at the first of each month). You have $10,000 available cash for the investment. You realize that buying a house involves some risk, so you are planning the move only if you can make a sizable profit on the deal (15% annual rate).

After checking with a real estate agent, you find that you can buy the house by placing $10,000 down and assuming a $25,000 mortgage. You figure that your expenses, including mortgage payments, will be about $250 per month. You expect to keep the property for 10 years, sell the property, pay off the mortgage, and net $20,000. Ignoring taxes, should you invest in the house?

You are dealing here with two types of cash flows: one, the income produced by the property (the monthly rental payments and the $20,000 profit from selling the house in ten years), and, two, the expenses of buying the house (the monthly mortgage payment, taxes, insurance, maintenance and down payment). To solve the problem, follow this procedure:

1. Find the present value of the income (steps 3 and 4).
2. Find the present value of the expenses (steps 5 and 6).
3. Compare the expenses to the income to see which is greater (step 7).

If the present value of the income equals or exceeds the present value of the expenses, you should buy the house.

Procedure	Press		Display
1. Clear calculator and mode registers; select two decimal places.	[ON/C] [STO] [2nd] [CMR] [FIX] 2		0.00
2. Select financial mode ("FIN" shows in the display).	[2nd] [Mode]	FIN	0.00
3. Calculate present value of monthly payments.			
a. Calculate and enter number of periods.	10 [×] 12 [=] [N]	FIN	120.00

Procedure	Press		Display
b. Calculate and enter desired monthly interest rate (use this as a discount factor in finding the present values).	15 [÷] 12 [=] [%i]	FIN	**1.25**
c. Enter monthly rental income and compute present value (an annuity due situation, since lease payments are usually made at the beginning of each period).	375 [PMT]	FIN	**375.00**
	[DUE] [PV] [STO]	FIN	**23534.11**
4. Calculate present value of sales price.			
a. Enter 0 (zero) for payment and enter amount of profit on sale.	0 [PMT]	FIN	**0.00**
	20000 [FV]	FIN	**20000.00**
b. Compute present value and add to monthly payment present value.	[2nd] [PV] [SUM]	FIN	**4504.29**
5. Enter monthly expenses (mortgage payment, taxes, insurance, and maintenance) and compute present value (an ordinary annuity).	250 [PMT]	FIN	**250.00**
	[2nd] [PV]	FIN	**15495.71**
6. Add down payment to find total present value of expenses.	[+] 10000 [=]	FIN	**25495.71**
7. Compare to present value of income.	[+/−] [+] [RCL] [=]	FIN	**2542.69**

Purchasing the house will give you more than the 15% annual return you want — by $2542.69.

CHAPTER 5

Indicated Overall Capitalization Rate Using Mortgage Constant

What is the present value of a $500,000 office complex? A survey of the records indicates that the predicted level net income stream of $35,000 annually is valid. It is possible to obtain a 75% mortgage at 10.25% for a term of 25 years, payable monthly. An equity yield rate of 13% is required.

One of the procedures used by real estate practitioners to derive an overall capitalization rate is described below. This rate is then used to determine an income-producing property's value.

1. Determine the annual mortgage constant, steps 3 through 7.
2. Solve for the indicated overall rate which is the following sum: (mortgage × mortgage constant) + (equity × desired equity yield), step 8.
3. Calculate the present value by $\frac{\text{net operating income}}{\text{overall rate}}$, step 9.

Procedure	Press		Display
1. Clear calculator and mode registers; select two decimal places.	[ON/C] [STO] [2nd] [CMR] [FIX] 2		**0.00**
2. Select financial mode ("FIN" shows in the display).	[2nd] [Mode]	FIN	**0.00**
3. Calculate and enter number of periods.	25 [×] 12 [=] [N]	FIN	**300.00**
4. Calculate and enter periodic interest rate.	10.25 [÷] 12 [=] [%i]	FIN	**0.85**

Indicated Overall Capitalization Rate Using Mortgage Constant

Procedure	Press		Display
5. Enter 1 as present value.	1 [PV]	FIN	**1.00**
6. Compute periodic mortgage constant.	[2nd] [PMT]	FIN	**0.01**
7. Multiply by number of periods per year to calculate annual mortgage constant.	[×] 12 [=]	FIN	**0.11**
8. Calculate indicated overall rate.	[×] .75 [=] [STO] .25 [×] .13 [+] [RCL] [=]	FIN	**0.12**
9. Calculate reciprocal and multiply by annual income to find present value of property.	[1/x] [×] 35000 [=]	FIN	**302050.94**

These calculations indicate that the property is worth no more than $302,051, assuming that the 13% equity yield rate must be met.

Reference:

Kinnard, *Income Property Valuation.*

CHAPTER

5 Calculating Capitalization Rates and Rates of Return

You are an investor who has paid $300,000 for a small office building. This income-producing property yields a level yearly net operating income of $30,000. This income should continue another 10 years. You have obtained a 30-year, 9 1/2% level monthly mortgage for $240,000. The property is to be sold in 10 years for an anticipated 80% of its original purchase price.

Calculate: 1. Overall capitalization rate = $\frac{\text{Net Operating Income}}{\text{Total Property Investment}}$

2. Cash throw-off before taxes = Net Operating Income − Annual Debt Service

3. Equity dividend rate (before taxes) = $\frac{\text{Cash throw-off}}{\text{Equity Investment}}$, where equity investment = property value − mortgage

4. Capital recovery amount per year for 10-year period = $\frac{\text{purchase price} - \text{selling price}}{\text{number of years}}$

Procedure	Press		Display
1. Clear calculator and mode registers; select two decimal places.	[ON/C] [STO] [2nd] [CMR] [FIX] 2		**0.00**
2. Select financial mode ("FIN" shows in the display).	[2nd] [Mode]	FIN	**0.00**

Calculating Capitalization Rates and Rates of Return

Procedure	Press		Display
3. Calculate overall capitalization rate.	30000 [÷] 300000 [=]	FIN	**0.10**
4. Calculate and enter number of periods.	30 [×] 12 [=] [N]	FIN	**360.00**
5. Calculate and enter periodic interest rate.	9.5 [÷] 12 [=] [%i]	FIN	**0.79**
6. Enter mortgage amount as present value.	240000 [PV]	FIN	**240000.00**
7. Compute monthly payment.	[2nd] [PMT]	FIN	**2018.05**
8. Multiply by number of periods per year to calculate annual debt service.	[×] 12 [=]	FIN	**24216.60**
9. Calculate and store annual cash throw-off.	[+/-] [+] 30000 [=] [STO]	FIN	**5783.40**
10. Calculate equity investment.	300000 [-] 240000 [=]	FIN	**60000.00**
11. Calculate equity dividend rate.	[EXC] [÷] [RCL] [=]	FIN	**0.10**
12. Calculate capital to be recovered.	300000 [-] 80 [%] [=]	FIN	**60000.00**
13. Divide by number of years to calculate capital recovery amount per year on a straight line basis.	[÷] 10 [=]	FIN	**6000.00**

The overall capitalization rate is 10%, the cash throw-off is $5783.40, the equity dividend rate is 10%, and the capital recovery amount is $6,000 per year.

CHAPTER 5

Leased Fee and Leasehold Valuations

Mrs. Willow leases a vacant lot to Mr. Oak for $10,000 per year for 50 years. Mr. Oak erects a building on the lot at a cost of $200,000 with a 50-year economic life. He then leases space in the building to several tenants, and his net income from the building is $20,000 annually. The land reversion value (FV) is $250,000. Using a 5% annual rate for Mrs. Willow and a 7% rate for Mr. Oak, determine the values of the leased fee and leasehold. (Assume that all lease payments are made at the beginning of each period.)

The leased fee valuation (steps 3 through 10) is the sum of the present value of the rent paid to the owner and the present value of the reversion (future) value of the property. Leasehold valuation (steps 11 through 14) is the present value of the annual rents paid by tenants to the leased fee holder minus the building costs.

Procedure	Press		Display
1. Clear calculator and mode registers; select two decimal places.	ON/C STO 2nd CMR FIX 2		**0.00**
2. Select financial mode ("FIN" shows in the display).	2nd Mode	FIN	**0.00**
3. Enter number of periods.	50 N	FIN	**50.00**
4. Enter Mrs. Willow's rate of return.	5 %i	FIN	**5.00**
5. Enter Mrs. Willow's rent income.	10000 PMT	FIN	**10000.00**
6. Compute and store present value of rents.	DUE PV STO	FIN	**191687.22**
7. Enter reversion value of property.	250000 FV	FIN	**250000.00**
8. Enter 0 (zero) as payment.	0 PMT	FIN	**0.00**
9. Compute present value of land's reversion value and add to memory.	2nd PV SUM	FIN	**21800.93**

Procedure	Press		Display
10. Recall leased fee value (annual rent income + reversion value).	RCL	FIN	**213488.15**
11. Enter Mr. Oak's rate of return.	7 %i	FIN	**7.00**
12. Enter Mr. Oak's annual income from building rentals.	20000 PMT	FIN	**20000.00**
13. Compute present value of Mr. Oak's income.	DUE PV	FIN	**295335.97**
14. Subtract cost of building to find leasehold value.	− 200000 =	FIN	**95335.97**

The leasehold value exceeds the value of the building by $95,335.97. This excess rental makes the business venture worthwhile.

Projecting Income and After-Tax Cash Flows

Assume that you are evaluating a property which will produce the following net operating income (cash revenues less cash operating expenses), excluding mortgage payments or depreciation deductions.

Year	1	2	3	4
Net Operating Income	$25,500	$29,000	$33,000	$36,000

The property will cost $200,000 with depreciable assets worth $140,000. These assets have a depreciation life of 30 years, with no salvage value, and are depreciated by the sum-of-the-years'-digits method.

To purchase the property, you need to invest $50,000 and borrow an additional $150,000 for 30 years at an annual interest rate of 14.5% compounded monthly. The monthly payment is $1836.83 and your tax rate is 48%.

For each of the next four years, project the net income before tax, the tax liability, and the after-tax cash flow.

The annual depreciation expense values are computed as illustrated in "Sum-of-the-Years'-Digits" in Chapter 4, and the annual interest paid on the mortgage is calculated as explained in "Total Amount of Interest Paid" in Chapter 7. The calculated values are:

Year	1	2	3	4
Annual Depreciation Expense	9032.26	8731.18	8430.11	8129.03
Annual Interest Paid	21729.79	21681.40	21625.50	21560.93

Procedure	**Press**	**Display**
1. Clear calculator and mode registers; select two decimal places.	[ON/C] [STO] [FIX] 2	**0.00**
2. Calculate and store annual mortgage payments.	1836.83 [×] 12 [=] [STO]	**22041.96**

Procedure	Press	Display
3. Calculations for year 1:		
a. Calculate net income before tax (net operating income − depreciation − interest paid).	25500 [−] 9032.26 [−] 21729.79 [=]	**-5262.05**
b. Multiply by tax rate to compute tax liability.	[×] 48 [%] [=]	**-2525.78**
c. Subtract tax liability (step 3b), add net operating income, and subtract annual mortgage payments to calculate after-tax cash flow.	[+/−] [+] 25500 [−] [RCL] [=]	**5983.82**
4. Calculations for year 2:		
a. Calculate net income before tax.	29000 [−] 8731.18 [−] 21681.40 [=]	**-1412.58**
b. Compute tax liability.	[×] 48 [%] [=]	**-678.04**
c. Calculate after-tax cash flow.	[+/−] [+] 29000 [−] [RCL] [=]	**7636.08**
5. Calculations for year 3:		
a. Calculate net income before tax.	33000 [−] 8430.11 [−] 21625.50 [=]	**2944.39**
b. Compute tax liability.	[×] 48 [%] [=]	**1413.31**
c. Calculate after-tax cash flow.	[+/−] [+] 33000 [−] [RCL] [=]	**9544.73**
6. Calculations for year 4:		
a. Calculate net income before tax.	36000 [−] 8129.03 [−] 21560.93 [=]	**6310.04**
b. Compute tax liability.	[×] 48 [%] [=]	**3028.82**
c. Calculate after-tax cash flow.	[+/−] [+] 36000 [−] [RCL] [=]	**10929.22**

Reference:

Hoagland, Stone, and Brueggeman, *Real Estate Finance,* Chapter 11.

Canadian Mortgages

Some Canadian mortgages require monthly payments with interest compounded semiannually instead of monthly. For example, you borrow $60,000 for 20 years with an annual interest rate of 13% compounded semiannually. How much is each monthly payment? If you pay 3 points, find the actual annual interest rate compounded semiannually.

The following is a general outline of the solution procedure:

1. Convert the interest rate per compounding period to the interest rate per payment period (step 3) as explained in "Finding the Future Value of an Annuity Where Compounding Periods and Payment Periods Are Not Equal" in Chapter 3.
2. Find the monthly payment amount using the interest rate per payment period (steps 4 through 6).
3. Compute the interest rate per payment period on the borrowed amount (steps 7 and 8).
4. Convert the rate per payment period on the borrowed amount to the rate per compounding period (step 9) as described in "Determining the Interest Rate Where Compounding Periods and Payment Periods Are Not Equal" in Chapter 3.

Procedure	Press		Display
1. Clear calculator and mode registers; select two decimal places.	[ON/C] [2nd] [CMR] [FIX] 2		**0.00**
2. Select financial mode ("FIN" shows in the display).	[2nd] [Mode]	FIN	**0.00**

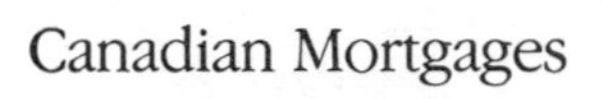

Procedure	Press		Display
3. Convert interest rate per compounding period to rate per payment period.			
a. Enter number of compounding periods per year.	2 [N]	FIN	**2.00**
b. Calculate and enter interest rate per compounding period.	13 [÷] 2 [=] [%i]	FIN	**6.50**
c. Enter 1 (one) for present value.	1 [PV]	FIN	**1.00**
d. Compute future value.	[2nd] [FV]	FIN	**1.13**
e. Enter number of payments per year.	12 [N]	FIN	**12.00**
f. Compute interest rate per payment period.	[2nd] [%i]	FIN	**1.06**
4. Calculate and enter number of payments.	20 [×] 12 [=] [N]	FIN	**240.00**
5. Enter amount borrowed.	60000 [PV]	FIN	**60000.00**
6. Compute payment amount.	[2nd] [PMT]	FIN	**688.52**
7. Calculate amount borrowed minus points and enter as present value.	60000 [-] 3 [%] [=] [PV]	FIN	**58200.00**
8. Compute interest rate per payment period.	[2nd] [%i]	FIN	**1.10**

(continued on next page)

Procedure	Press		Display
9. Convert interest rate per payment period to rate per compounding period.			
a. Enter number of payments per year.	12 [N]	FIN	**12.00**
b. Enter 0 (zero) for payment.	0 [PMT]	FIN	**0.00**
c. Enter 1 (one) for present value.	1 [PV]	FIN	**1.00**
d. Compute future value.	[2nd] [FV]	FIN	**1.14**
e. Enter number of compounding periods per year.	2 [N]	FIN	**2.00**
f. Compute interest rate per compounding period.	[2nd] [%i]	FIN	**6.76**
10. Multiply by number of compounding periods per year to calculate annual interest rate.	[×] 2 [=]	FIN	**13.53**

The monthly payment is $688.52, and by paying 3 points the interest rate increased from 13% to an actual rate of 13.53%.

Reference:

Greynolds, Aronofsky, and Frame, *Financial Analysis Using Calculators: Time Value of Money,* p. 148.

CHAPTER 6

LEASES

The profitability of a personal or business-related lease is affected by many factors, such as payment amount, required return rate, residual value, and alternate investment opportunities. Before actually entering into any lease agreement, all factors should be carefully evaluated. With your calculator, you can quickly explore various types of leasing arrangements and use the results to make more informed decisions.

In this chapter we have included the following examples:

- leases with and without residual values (value of an asset at the end of a lease)
- leases with advance payments made with the first payment
- leases with variable payments instead of constant payments
- business-related lease-or-buy decisions, including decisions about whether or not to acquire the equipment
- personal lease-or-buy decisions
- amortization of a lease.

Finding the Present Value of a Lease without a Residual Value

On January 1, Howard and Dorothy's Bakery signed a five-year lease for a kneading machine. The annual payments are $2,500, payable at the beginning of each year. Using an annual interest rate of 7%, what is the present value of the lease? (Since the payments are made at the beginning of each period, this is an annuity due situation.)

Procedure	Press		Display
1. Clear calculator and mode registers; select two decimal places.	[ON/C] [2nd] [CMR] [FIX] 2		0.00
2. Select financial mode ("FIN" shows in the display).	[2nd] [Mode]	FIN	0.00
3. Enter number of payment periods (years).	5 [N]	FIN	5.00
4. Enter periodic interest rate.	7 [%i]	FIN	7.00
5. Enter periodic payment.	2500 [PMT]	FIN	2500.00
6. Compute present value of lease.	[DUE] [PV]	FIN	**10968.03**

The lease has a present value of $10,968.03.

CHAPTER 6

Finding the Payment Amount of a Lease without a Residual Value

Your company is leasing a warehouse to Smilin' Sam's Storage Company for twelve months, beginning January 1 of next year. The present value of the lease payments must be $75,000 to give you a minimum annual return of 11.5%. Payments are due on the first of each month. Ignoring tax effects, what must the monthly payments be?

Procedure	Press		Display
1. Clear calculator and mode registers; select two decimal places.	[ON/C] [2nd] [CMR] [FIX] 2		0.00
2. Select financial mode ("FIN" shows in the display).	[2nd] [Mode]	FIN	0.00
3. Enter number of payment periods (months).	12 [N]	FIN	12.00
4. Calculate and enter periodic interest rate.	11.5 [÷] 12 [=] [%i]	FIN	0.96
5. Enter present value.	75000 [PV]	FIN	75000.00
6. Compute periodic payment.	[DUE] [PMT]	FIN	**6583.04**

Monthly payments of $6583.04 fulfill the 11.5% annual return requirement.

Finding the Interest Rate on a Lease without a Residual Value

Your company is considering leasing a machine which can be bought outright for $49,000. The lease requires 24 payments of $2,300 at the beginning of each month. What interest rate is the lessor charging?

Procedure	Press		Display
1. Clear calculator and mode registers; select two decimal places.	[ON/C] [2nd] [CMR] [FIX] 2		**0.00**
2. Select financial mode ("FIN" shows in the display).	[2nd] [Mode]	FIN	**0.00**
3. Enter number of periods (months).	24 [N]	FIN	**24.00**
4. Enter periodic payment.	2300 [PMT]	FIN	**2300.00**
5. Enter purchase price of machine.	49000 [PV]	FIN	**49000.00**
6. Compute periodic interest rate.	[DUE] [%i]	FIN	**1.07**
7. Multiply by number of payments per year to calculate annual interest rate.	[×] 12 [=]	FIN	**12.78**

The lessor is charging an annual interest rate of 12.78%.

Finding the Number of Payments on a Lease without a Residual Value

The Berty Company has offered to lease a specialized pipe machine from the Jans Company for $1500 to be paid at the beginning of each month. Jans requires an annual interest rate of 20% compounded monthly as a return on machine leases. The machine's current market value is $40,000. How many monthly payments are necessary for Jans to earn a return of at least 20%?

Procedure	Press		Display
1. Clear calculator and mode registers; select two decimal places.	[ON/C] [2nd] [CMR] [FIX] 2		**0.00**
2. Select financial mode ("FIN" shows in the display).	[2nd] [Mode]	FIN	**0.00**
3. Calculate and enter periodic interest rate.	20 [÷] 12 [=] [%i]	FIN	**1.67**
4. Enter amount of periodic payment.	1500 [PMT]	FIN	**1500.00**
5. Enter present value of asset.	40000 [PV]	FIN	**40000.00**
6. Compute number of payments.	[DUE] [N]	FIN	**34.77**

The Jans Company will earn slightly more than 20% if the Berty Company makes 35 monthly payments of $1500.

Determining the Payment Amount of a Lease with a Residual Value

The JQ Company is leasing a machine with a current market value of $130,000 to the RO Company for three years. At the end of this time, the machine's market value should be $90,000. Lease payments are to be made at the beginning of each quarter. If the JQ Company wants to earn an annual return rate of 25% compounded quarterly, how much should the quarterly payments be?

The procedure for solving the problem is:

1. Compute the present value of the machine's residual value (steps 3 through 6).
2. Determine the net present value (step 7).
3. Calculate the payment amount required for the lease (step 8).

Procedure	Press		Display
1. Clear calculator and mode registers; select two decimal places.	[ON/C] [2nd] [CMR] [FIX] 2		**0.00**
2. Select financial mode ("FIN" shows in the display).	[2nd] [Mode]	FIN	**0.00**
3. Calculate and enter number of periods.	3 [×] 4 [=] [N]	FIN	**12.00**
4. Calculate and enter periodic interest rate.	25 [÷] 4 [=] [%i]	FIN	**6.25**
5. Enter residual value of asset.	90000 [FV]	FIN	**90000.00**
6. Compute present value of residual.	[2nd] [PV]	FIN	**43480.57**
7. Subtract displayed value from current market value to calculate net present value.	[+/−] [+] 130000 [=] [PV]	FIN	**86519.43**
8. Compute amount of payment.	[DUE] [PMT]	FIN	**9846.30**

For the JQ Company to earn an annual interest rate of 25% compounded quarterly, the RO Company must make quarterly payments of $9846.30.

CHAPTER 6

Determining the Present Value of a Lease with a Residual Value

The Peach Bright Company wants to purchase a machine which it is currently leasing from your company. You offer to sell the machine for the equivalent present value of the lease discounted at an annual interest rate of 22% compounded monthly. The machine has a residual value of $6500, and 46 monthly payments of $1200 remain on the lease. If the payments are due at the beginning of each month, how much should you charge for the machine?

The total value of the machine is the sum of the present value of the residual value (steps 3 through 6) and the present value of the lease payments (steps 7 and 8).

Procedure	Press		Display
1. Clear calculator and mode registers; select two decimal places.	[ON/C] [STO] [2nd] [CMR] [FIX] 2		**0.00**
2. Select financial mode ("FIN" shows in the display).	[2nd] [Mode]	FIN	**0.00**
3. Enter number of payments.	46 [N]	FIN	**46.00**
4. Calculate and enter periodic interest rate.	22 [÷] 12 [=] [%i]	FIN	**1.83**

Determining the Present Value of a Lease with a Residual Value

Procedure	Press		Display
5. Enter residual value of asset.	6500 [FV]	FIN	**6500.00**
6. Compute and store present value of residual.	[2nd] [PV] [STO]	FIN	**2818.22**
7. Enter amount of lease payment.	1200 [PMT]	FIN	**1200.00**
8. Compute present value of lease payments.	[DUE] [PV]	FIN	**37754.96**
9. Add present value of residual (step 6) to calculate present value of lease.	[+] [RCL] [=]	FIN	**40573.18**

Peach Bright should pay your company $40,573.18 for the machine.

CHAPTER 6

Determining the Interest Rate on a Lease with a Residual Value

You lease a $10,400 automobile for 36 months and pay $303.54 at the beginning of each month. If the automobile has an assumed residual value of $3,500, find the annual interest rate, compounded monthly.

Since the annuity equation cannot directly solve for the interest rate, the solution must be found by a repetitive, trial-and-error process known as an iteration. See steps 4 through 14.

Procedure	Press		Display
1. Clear calculator and mode registers; select two decimal places.	[ON/C] [STO] [2nd] [CMR] [FIX] 2		**0.00**
2. Select financial mode ("FIN" shows in the display).	[2nd] [Mode]	FIN	**0.00**
3. Enter number of periods.	36 [N]	FIN	**36.00**
4. Enter payment amount and subtract market value; store result.	303.54 [−] 10400 [=] [STO]	FIN	**-10096.46**
5. Calculate and enter future value (market value − residual value ÷ step 4 value × 100).	10400 [−] 3500 [÷] [RCL] [×] 100 [=] [FV]	FIN	**-68.34**
6. Calculate and store (payment amount ÷ step 4 value × 100).	303.54 [÷] [RCL] [×] 100 [=] [STO]	FIN	**-3.01**

Determining the Interest Rate on a Lease with a Residual Value

Procedure	Press		Display
7. Enter first estimate for %i. (Use the value calculated in step 6 or your own estimate.)	[%i]	FIN	**-3.01**
8. Calculate second estimate for %i.	[2nd] [PMT] [−] [RCL] [=] [%i]	FIN	**-0.08**
9. Calculate third estimate.	[2nd] [PMT] [−] [RCL] [=] [%i]	FIN	**1.08**
10. Calculate fourth estimate.	[2nd] [PMT] [−] [RCL] [=] [%i]	FIN	**1.44**
11. Calculate fifth estimate.	[2nd] [PMT] [−] [RCL] [=] [%i]	FIN	**1.55**
12. Calculate sixth estimate.	[2nd] [PMT] [−] [RCL] [=] [%i]	FIN	**1.57**
13. Calculate seventh estimate.	[2nd] [PMT] [−] [RCL] [=] [%i]	FIN	**1.58**
14. Calculate eighth estimate.*	[2nd] [PMT] [−] [RCL] [=] [%i]	FIN	**1.58**
15. Multiply by number of payments per year to calculate annual interest rate.	[×] 12 [=]	FIN	**18.99**

The annual interest rate on the automobile is 18.99% compounded monthly.

*To find the interest rate with this procedure, repeat the key sequence for estimating the interest rate (steps 8 through 14) until the displayed answer equals the previous answer or until the answer reaches your desired level of accuracy. Notice that, in this case, the eighth estimate equals the seventh estimate so the iteration is complete in step 14. You might want to display more decimal places to increase the level of accuracy.

CHAPTER 6

Determining the Present Value of a Lease with Advance Payments

The Fortune Company is trying to decide whether to lease or buy a machine from the Two Star Company. The lease agreement would require Fortune to make payments of $1,850 at the beginning of each month for eight years and to make two advance payments to replace the last two regular payments. Two Star is willing to sell the machine for a price equivalent to the present value of a lease which would earn 17% annual interest, compounded monthly. How much should Two Star charge for the machine? (Assume that the residual value is zero.)

Advance payments are payments made in addition to the first regular payment. The amount of each advance payment equals the amount of each regular payment. These payments usually replace a corresponding number of payments at the end of the lease term.

The net present value of the machine is the sum of the present value of the lease payments (steps 3 through 6) and the advance payments (step 7).

Procedure	Press		Display
1. Clear calculator and mode registers; select two decimal places.	ON/C STO 2nd CMR FIX 2		0.00
2. Select financial mode ("FIN" shows in the display).	2nd Mode	FIN	0.00

Determining the Present Value of a Lease with Advance Payments

Procedure	Press		Display
3. Calculate and enter number of periods, excluding advance payments.	8 [×] 12 [−] 2 [=] [N]	FIN	**94.00**
4. Calculate and enter periodic interest rate.	17 [÷] 12 [=] [%i]	FIN	**1.42**
5. Enter amount of payment.	1850 [PMT]	FIN	**1850.00**
6. Compute and store present value.	[DUE] [PV] [STO]	FIN	**97141.37**
7. Calculate amount of advance payments.	2 [×] 1850 [=]	FIN	**3700.00**
8. Add present value of lease payments to calculate present value of lease.	[+] [RCL] [=]	FIN	**100841.37**

The Two Star Company should charge $100,841.37 for the machine in order to earn an annual return of 17% compounded quarterly.

Reference:

Greynolds, Aronofsky, and Frame, *Financial Analysis Using Calculators: Time Value of Money,* pp. 400-401.

CHAPTER 6

Determining the Payment Amount for a Lease with Advance Payments

The Boxer Company is leasing a machine to the Framing Company for four years. The machine has a current market value of $100,000 and no residual value. Boxer is asking Framing to make one regular payment and three advance payments when the lease is signed. If Boxer wants a return equal to an annual interest rate of 18% compounded monthly, how much is each monthly payment?

You can solve the problem with this method:

1. With a periodic payment of $1, compute the present value of the annuity due (steps 3 through 6).
2. Add the number of advance payments (step 7), and divide the current market value by the previous result to calculate the payment amount (step 8).

Procedure	Press		Display
1. Clear calculator and mode registers; select two decimal places.	[ON/C] [2nd] [CMR] [FIX] 2		**0.00**
2. Select financial mode ("FIN" shows in the display).	[2nd] [Mode]	FIN	**0.00**
3. Calculate and enter number of regular payments, excluding advance payments.	4 [×] 12 [−] 3 [=] [N]	FIN	**45.00**
4. Calculate and enter periodic interest rate.	18 [÷] 12 [=] [%i]	FIN	**1.50**
5. Enter 1 (one) for payment.	1 [PMT]	FIN	**1.00**
6. Compute present value.	[DUE] [PV]	FIN	**33.04**
7. Add number of advance payments and store result.	[+] 3 [=] [STO]	FIN	**36.04**
8. Divide current market value by previous result to find amount of payment.	100000 [÷] [RCL] [=]	FIN	**2774.65**

The Framing Company should make monthly payments of $2774.65.

Determining the Interest Rate for a Lease with Advance Payments

The Flower Company is leasing a special purpose machine to the Seed Company for nine years, with payments of $14,000 due at the beginning of each quarter. In addition to the first payment, the Seed Company must make four advance payments to replace the last four regular payments. If the current value of the machine is $250,000 and the residual value is zero, what annual rate of return, compounded quarterly, is Flower earning?

Procedure	Press		Display
1. Clear calculator and mode registers; select two decimal places.	[ON/C] [2nd] [CMR] [FIX] 2		0.00
2. Select financial mode ("FIN" shows in the display).	[2nd] [Mode]	FIN	0.00
3. Calculate and enter number of periods, excluding advance payments.	9 [×] 4 [−] 4 [=] [N]	FIN	32.00
4. Enter amount of payment.	14000 [PMT]	FIN	14000.00
5. Calculate amount of advance payments.	4 [×] 14000 [=]	FIN	56000.00
6. Deduct displayed value from current asset value and enter as present value.	[+/−] [+] 250000 [=] [PV]	FIN	194000.00
7. Compute periodic interest rate.	[DUE] [%i]	FIN	6.75
8. Multiply by number of payments per year to calculate annual interest rate.	[×] 4 [=]	FIN	27.01

The Flower Company is earning 27.01% annual interest, compounded quarterly.

CHAPTER

6 Computing the Present Value of a Lease with Variable Payments

Your company has the option of leasing a machine for six years or buying it, with the purchase price being equal to the present value of the lease payments discounted by an 11% annual rate. The payments, payable at the beginning of each year, are:

Year	1	2	3	4	5	6
Lease Payments	$16,000	$15,500	$14,500	$13,500	$12,500	$11,000

Ignoring tax effects, what is the purchase price of the machine (the present value of the lease payments)?

"Time lines" can help you visualize a financial situation such as this one. A time line is usually drawn as a horizontal line divided into equal intervals representing the interest discounting periods. The time line for this example is illustrated here:

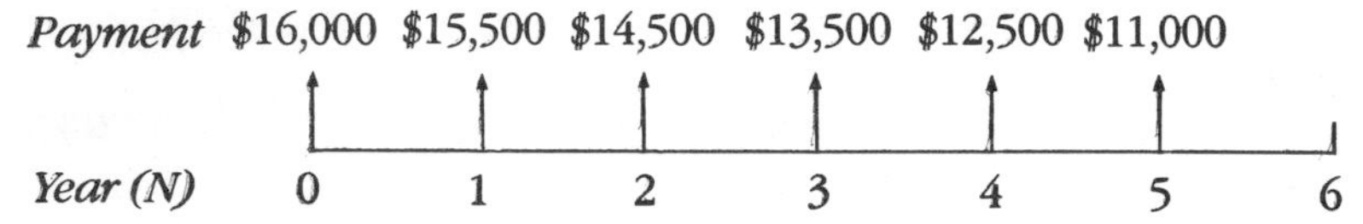

Notice that since each payment occurs at the *beginning* of the year, the year shown on the time line (N) is one less than the year number when the payment is made. This means that the second payment is discounted for one period; the third, for two periods; etc.

To calculate the purchase price of the machine, find the total of the present values of the lease payments.

Procedure	Press		Display
1. Clear calculator and mode registers; select two decimal places.	ON/C STO 2nd CMR FIX 2		**0.00**
2. Select financial mode ("FIN" shows in the display).	2nd Mode	FIN	**0.00**
3. Enter periodic interest rate.	11 %i	FIN	**11.00**
4. Calculate present value of year 2 lease payment.			
a. Enter period number.	1 N	FIN	**1.00**
b. Enter payment amount.	15500 FV	FIN	**15500.00**

Computing the Present Value of a Lease with Variable Payments

Procedure	Press		Display
c. Compute and store present value.	[2nd] [PV] [STO]	FIN	**13963.96**
5. Calculate present value of year 3 lease payment.			
a. Enter period number.	2 [N]	FIN	**2.00**
b. Enter payment amount.	14500 [FV]	FIN	**14500.00**
c. Compute present value and add to memory.	[2nd] [PV] [SUM]	FIN	**11768.53**
6. Calculate present value of year 4 lease payment.			
a. Enter period number.	3 [N]	FIN	**3.00**
b. Enter payment amount.	13500 [FV]	FIN	**13500.00**
c. Compute present value and add to memory.	[2nd] [PV] [SUM]	FIN	**9871.08**
7. Calculate present value of year 5 lease payment.			
a. Enter period number.	4 [N]	FIN	**4.00**
b. Enter payment amount.	12500 [FV]	FIN	**12500.00**
c. Compute present value and add to memory.	[2nd] [PV] [SUM]	FIN	**8234.14**
8. Calculate present value of year 6 lease payment.			
a. Enter period number.	5 [N]	FIN	**5.00**
b. Enter payment amount.	11000 [FV]	FIN	**11000.00**
c. Compute present value and add to memory.	[2nd] [PV] [SUM]	FIN	**6527.96**
9. Add year 1 payment amount.	16000 [SUM]	FIN	**16000.00**
10. Recall present value total.	[RCL]	FIN	**66365.67**

The purchase price of this particular machine is $66,365.67.

CHAPTER 6

A Simplified Business Lease-or-Buy Decision

Your business is considering buying or leasing a new computer. According to the lease agreement, you would pay $36,000 per year for five years at the first of each year. On the other hand, you could buy the machine (with a five year service contract) for $125,000. If the computer is installed, it is expected to save your company $46,000 per year. You have determined that the computer will have no resale value at the end of the five years. Ignoring tax effects, should you acquire the computer, and if so, should you lease it or purchase it?

Your company is a healthy one with good credit and can borrow at 15% annual interest. You require a 20% annual return on projects and investments of this kind.

Procedure	Press		Display
1. Clear calculator and mode registers; select two decimal places.	ON/C 2nd CMR FIX 2		0.00
2. Select financial mode ("FIN" shows in the display).	2nd Mode	FIN	0.00
3. Enter number of periods.	5 N	FIN	5.00
4. Enter required annual return rate.	20 %i	FIN	20.00
5. Enter annual savings.	46000 PMT	FIN	46000.00
6. Compute present value of savings.	2nd PV	FIN	**137568.16**

The present value of the annual savings exceeds the purchase price of the computer, so the investment will exceed your annual required return rate. Acquiring the computer is a good financial move. Next, determine whether you want to lease it or buy it.

A Simplified Business Lease-or-Buy Decision

Procedure	Press		Display
7. Clear calculator and mode registers.	[ON/C] [2nd] [CMR]	FIN	**0.00**
8. Enter number of periods.	5 [N]	FIN	**5.00**
9. Enter periodic interest rate at which your firm can borrow.	15 [%i]	FIN	**15.00**
10. Enter annual lease payment.	36000 [PMT]	FIN	**36000.00**
11. Compute present value of lease payments.	[DUE] [PV]	FIN	**138779.22**

The present value of the lease payments is greater than the purchase price of the computer ($125,000), so it would be best to buy the computer outright.

Amortizing a Lease

A firm has leased some equipment for four years and has agreed to pay the annual $5000 lease at the beginning of each yearly period. Assuming an annual discount rate of 16%, prepare a leasehold amortization schedule for this equipment.

Procedure	Press		Display
1. Clear calculator and mode registers; select two decimal places.	ON/C 2nd CMR FIX 2		0.00
2. Select financial mode ("FIN" shows in the display).	2nd Mode	FIN	0.00
3. Enter number of payments.	4 N	FIN	4.00
4. Enter periodic discount rate.	16 %i	FIN	16.00
5. Enter payment amount.	5000 PMT	FIN	5000.00
6. Compute present value of lease payment.	DUE PV	FIN	16229.45
7. Calculate year 1 values:			
a. Calculate balance due after first payment and enter as present value for remainder of lease.	− 5000 = PV	FIN	11229.45
b. Add 1 to period number (annuity due).	1 + 1 =	FIN	2.00
c. Calculate principal.	2nd P/I	FIN	3203.29
d. Display interest.	x:y	FIN	1796.71

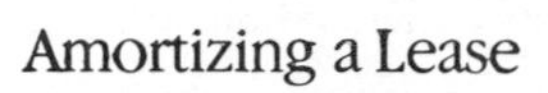

Procedure	Press		Display
8. Calculate year 2 values:			
a. Compute balance after second payment.	2 [2nd] [Acc/Bal] [x:y]	FIN	**8026.16**
b. Add 1 to period number (annuity due).	2 [+] 1 [=]	FIN	**3.00**
c. Calculate principal.	[2nd] [P/I]	FIN	**3715.81**
d. Display interest.	[x:y]	FIN	**1284.19**
9. Calculate year 3 values:			
a. Compute balance after third payment.	3 [2nd] [Acc/Bal] [x:y]	FIN	**4310.34**
b. Add 1 to period number (annuity due).	3 [+] 1 [=]	FIN	**4.00**
c. Calculate principal.	[2nd] [P/I]	FIN	**4310.34**
d. Display interest.	[x:y]	FIN	**689.66**
10. Calculate year 4 values:			
a. Compute balance after fourth payment.	4 [2nd] [Acc/Bal] [x:y]	FIN	**0.00**

A Personal Lease-or-Purchase Decision

The sale price of a car is $5000. You can purchase the car by making a $1000 down payment and financing the balance at 1% per month for three years (36 months). You figure that your maintenance costs will be $15 a month and that you can sell the car for $2500 at the end of the three years. Alternatively, you can lease a similar car for three years at $115 a month with the leasing company taking care of maintenance. The lease payments would be due at the beginning of the month. If your bank currently pays 5% annual interest, compounded monthly, which alternative would save you money in the long run?

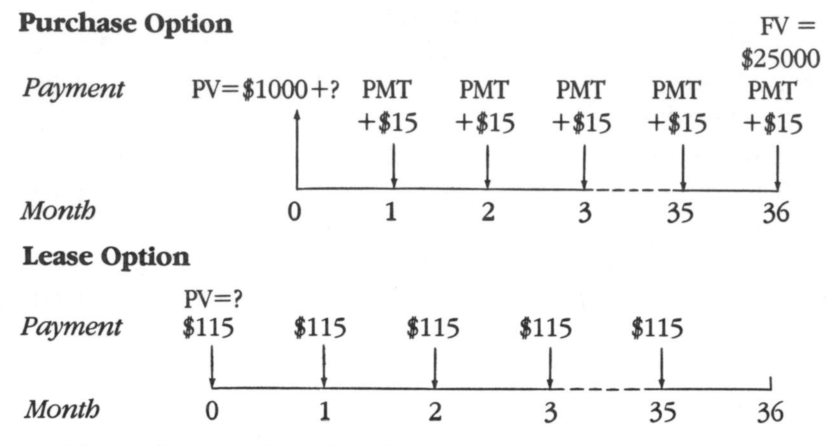

The problem can be solved by comparing the present value of the lease option to the present value of the purchase option. The present value of the purchase option can be determined as follows:

1. Find the monthly payment amount on the car loan (steps 3 through 6).
2. Compute the present value of the loan payment plus maintenance cost (steps 7 through 9). Add down payment to result (step 10).
3. Calculate the present value of the car's resale value (steps 11 through 13), and deduct from the present value of the cost of purchasing the car (step 14).

The present value of the lease option is the present value of the lease payments (steps 15 and 16).

	Procedure	Press		Display
1.	Clear calculator and mode registers; select two decimal places.	[ON/C] [STO] [2nd] [CMR] [FIX] 2		**0.00**
2.	Select financial mode ("FIN" shows in the display).	[2nd] [Mode]	FIN	**0.00**
3.	Enter number of periods.	36 [N]	FIN	**36.00**
4.	Enter loan's periodic interest rate.	1 [%i]	FIN	**1.00**
5.	Calculate and enter loan amount.	5000 [−] 1000 [=] [PV]	FIN	**4000.00**
6.	Compute monthly loan payment.	[2nd] [PMT]	FIN	**132.86**
7.	Add monthly maintenance cost.	[+] 15 [=] [PMT]	FIN	**147.86**
8.	Calculate and enter current interest rate on savings account.	5 [÷] 12 [=] [%i]	FIN	**0.42**
9.	Compute and store present value of monthly expenses.	[2nd] [PV] [STO]	FIN	**4933.36**
10.	Add down payment to memory.	1000 [SUM]	FIN	**1000.00**
11.	Enter 0 (zero) for payment.	0 [PMT]	FIN	**0.00**
12.	Enter resale value.	2500 [FV]	FIN	**2500.00**
13.	Compute present value.	[2nd] [PV]	FIN	**2152.44**

(continued on next page)

Procedure	Press		Display
14. Deduct displayed value from present value of monthly expenses stored in memory to calculate present value of cost of purchasing car; store result.	[+/−] [+] [RCL] [=] [STO]	FIN	**3780.92**
15. Enter amount of monthly lease payments.	115 [PMT]	FIN	**115.00**
16. Compute present value of lease payments.	[DUE] [PV]	FIN	**3853.04**
17. Compare present value of lease payments to present value of cost of car.	[−] [RCL] [=]	FIN	**72.12**

Based on these calculations, it costs $72.12 more to lease the car. Since this is a rather small difference, you can go on to weigh other reasons in favor of one decision or the other.

CHAPTER 7

LOANS

Even the most conservative spenders occasionally need to borrow money for special purchases. When you borrow money, you pay the lending institution a fee for using their money (interest). The amount of interest you pay depends on the percentage rate of interest, the length of time you borrow the money, and the way the interest is calculated. This chapter will help you evaluate various loan situations to determine which are the most economical.

Basically, interest rates are stated as either nominal or effective. An effective rate is the rate actually earned or paid for the specified time period, usually a year. The interest rate is generally stated as an effective rate in Europe. Nominal rates are most commonly used in the United States and are expressed as an annual rate. The annual rate divided by the number of compounding periods per year equals the periodic nominal rate. The Annual Percent Interest Rate (APR) is essentially the same as the annual nominal rate. For example, with a 12% APR, compounded monthly, the monthly interest rate used for compounding is 12% ÷ 12, or 1%, per month.

Some types of credit transactions exclude certain fees or discounts when determining the APR. When you are borrowing money, it's a good idea to find out what items, if any, are excluded from the APR calculation. If any fees are excluded, the annual nominal rate which you actually pay will be higher than the APR. Also when quoting an APR, lending institutions often round the rate to the nearest 1/4%. Therefore, if you enter the quoted rate in the calculations, your answer (such as the payment amount) may differ slightly from the amount calculated by the lender.

NOTE: The applications in this chapter assume that payments are made at the end of each payment period. Use your calculator to explore these sample problems and try these concepts on your personal financial situations. You may find that you're able to make better decisions and, hopefully, pay less for your money.

Amount to Borrow and Amount of Down Payment

You need to buy a new car which sells for $5,100. You can afford a monthly payment of $125, and the finance company charges 13.51% APR, compounded monthly. What loan and down payment amounts are required for a 48-month loan?

Procedure	Press		Display
1. Clear calculator and mode registers; select two decimal places.	[ON/C] [2nd] [CMR] [FIX] 2		**0.00**
2. Select financial mode ("FIN" shows in the display).	[2nd] [Mode]	FIN	**0.00**
3. Enter number of payment periods.	48 [N]	FIN	**48.00**
4. Calculate and enter periodic interest rate.	13.51 [÷] 12 [=] [%i]	FIN	**1.13**
5. Enter amount of payment.	125 [PMT]	FIN	**125.00**
6. Compute loan amount.	[2nd] [PV]	FIN	**4615.73**
7. Calculate down payment.	[+/-] [+] 5100 [=]	FIN	**484.27**

To buy the car you must make a $484.27 down payment and borrow $4,615.73.

CHAPTER 7

Amount of Payment

You are planning to purchase a new small desk and chair set which is sale priced at $525. You can finance your purchase at 20% APR, compounded monthly, for two years. How much is the monthly payment?

Procedure	Press		Display
1. Clear calculator and mode registers; select two decimal places.	[ON/C] [2nd] [CMR] [FIX] 2		**0.00**
2. Select financial mode ("FIN" shows in the display).	[2nd] [Mode]	FIN	**0.00**
3. Calculate and enter number of payment periods.	2 [×] 12 [=] [N]	FIN	**24.00**
4. Calculate and enter periodic interest rate.	20 [÷] 12 [=] [%i]	FIN	**1.67**
5. Enter loan amount.	525 [PV]	FIN	**525.00**
6. Compute payment.	[2nd] [PMT]	FIN	**26.72**

Your monthly payment will be $26.72.

Solving for the APR

A pickup truck sells for $4,817. To purchase the truck, you must make a down payment of $150 and 48 monthly payments of $127. The dealer quoted you an APR of 13.77%. Verify this quote.

	Procedure	Press		Display
1.	Clear calculator and mode registers; select two decimal places.	[ON/C] [2nd] [CMR] [FIX] 2		0.00
2.	Select financial mode ("FIN" shows in the display).	[2nd] [Mode]	FIN	0.00
3.	Enter number of payment periods.	48 [N]	FIN	48.00
4.	Enter amount of payment.	127 [PMT]	FIN	127.00
5.	Calculate and enter loan amount.	4817 [−] 150 [=] [PV]	FIN	4667.00
6.	Compute monthly interest rate.	[2nd] [%i]	FIN	1.15
7.	**Multiply by number of payments per year to calculate APR.**	[×] 12 [=]	FIN	13.77

The dealer quoted you the correct APR.

Determining Time Needed to Pay Off a Loan

You borrow $1900 to buy a used car at 12% APR, compounded monthly. With a monthly payment of $96.64, how long will it take you to pay off the loan?

Procedure	Press		Display
1. Clear calculator and mode registers; select two decimal places.	[ON/C] [2nd] [CMR] [FIX] 2		0.00
2. Select financial mode ("FIN" shows in the display).	[2nd] [Mode]	FIN	0.00
3. Calculate and enter periodic interest rate.	12 [÷] 12 [=] [%i]	FIN	1.00
4. Enter amount of payment.	96.64 [PMT]	FIN	96.64
5. Enter loan amount.	1900 [PV]	FIN	1900.00
6. Compute number of payment periods.	[2nd] [N]	FIN	**22.00**

You must make 22 monthly payments to pay off the loan.

Amount of Final Payment

Assume that you borrow $3,920 at a 15% APR, compounded monthly, with monthly payments of $175. How many payments will you make? How much is the final payment?

Procedure	Press		Display
1. Clear calculator and mode registers; select two decimal places.	[ON/C] [2nd] [CMR] [FIX] 2		**0.00**
2. Select financial mode ("FIN" shows in the display).	[2nd] [Mode]	FIN	**0.00**
3. Calculate and enter periodic interest rate.	15 [÷] 12 [=] [%i]	FIN	**1.25**
4. Enter amount of payment.	175 [PMT]	FIN	**175.00**
5. Enter loan amount.	3920 [PV]	FIN	**3920.00**
6. Compute number of payments.	[2nd] [N]	FIN	**26.44**
7. Enter whole number value from step 6 and calculate loan balance after last regular payment (payment 26).	26 [2nd] [Acc/Bal] [x:y]	FIN	**77.05**
8. Enter loan balance (step 7) as present value.*	[PV]	FIN	**77.05**
9. Enter 1 (one) for number of periods.	1 [N]	FIN	**1.00**
10. Enter 0 (zero) for payment.	0 [PMT]	FIN	**0.00**
11. Compute amount of final payment.	[2nd] [FV]	FIN	**78.01**

You will make a total of 27 payments, 26 payments of $175 and a final payment of $78.01.

*Since the loan balance ($77.05) will be paid with the next payment (payment 27), you can find the amount of the final payment by computing the future value of the loan balance.

Total Amount of Interest Paid

You borrow $4400 from your credit union to buy a car. The credit union charges 10.5% APR, compounded monthly, and you will repay the loan in 36 monthly payments. How much will it cost to borrow the $4400? (In other words, find the accumulated interest based on 36 payments.)

Procedure	Press		Display
1. Clear calculator and mode registers; select two decimal places.	[ON/C] [2nd] [CMR] [FIX] 2		**0.00**
2. Select financial mode ("FIN" shows in the display).	[2nd] [Mode]	FIN	**0.00**
3. Enter number of periods.	36 [N]	FIN	**36.00**
4. Calculate and enter periodic interest rate.	10.5 [÷] 12 [=] [%i]	FIN	**0.88**
5. Enter loan amount as present value.	4400 [PV]	FIN	**4400.00**
6. Compute periodic payment amount.	[2nd] [PMT]	FIN	**143.01**
7. Calculate accumulated interest at end of loan (36 payments).	36 [2nd] [Acc/Bal]	FIN	**748.39**

You will pay the credit union $748.39 in interest when you borrow $4400.

Comparing Time Payments

A salesman tells you that he will sell you the latest vacuum cleaner for payments of only $15 a month for three years at 21% APR. A store has advertised the same vacuum cleaner for $325. Which deal is best?

One way to evaluate the time payment purchase is to compute the present value of the series of payments at the interest rate quoted by the seller and compare that amount to the sale price of the item.

Procedure	Press		Display
1. Clear calculator and mode registers; select two decimal places.	[ON/C] [2nd] [CMR] [FIX] 2		**0.00**
2. Select financial mode ("FIN" shows in the display).	[2nd] [Mode]	FIN	**0.00**
3. Calculate and enter number of payments.	3 [×] 12 [=] [N]	FIN	**36.00**
4. Calculate and enter periodic interest rate.	21 [÷] 12 [=] [%i]	FIN	**1.75**
5. Enter payment amount.	15 [PMT]	FIN	**15.00**
6. Compute present value.	[2nd] [PV]	FIN	**398.14**

Compare this amount to the store's advertised price. The salesman's "deal" is not really a good one. The interest rate is too high.

CHAPTER 7

Converting Add-On Interest Rates to APR

Your lending institution is loaning a consumer $2500 for three years. According to state law, the highest rate you can charge is 8% add-on. Find the amount of the payment and the APR.

NOTE: Federal regulations require lenders to quote interest rates as APR. However, some states have usury laws stating interest rate ceilings in terms of add-on interest. As a result, many lenders need to convert add-on interest to APR and vice versa. The formula is:

$$\text{“Add-On” Interest} = \text{total amount financed} \times \text{add-on rate} \times \text{number of years}$$

where the add-on rate is expressed as a decimal. This gives the total amount of the interest paid for the loan. To figure payments, add the interest to the principal and divide the total by the number of payments. In other words, part of each payment is interest and the rest goes to pay back the principal.

Procedure	Press		Display
1. Clear calculator and mode registers; select two decimal places.	[ON/C] [STO] [2nd] [CMR] [FIX] 2		**0.00**
2. Select financial mode ("FIN" shows in the display).	[2nd] [Mode]	FIN	**0.00**
3. Calculate and enter number of periods.	3 [×] 12 [=] [N]	FIN	**36.00**
4. Enter and store total amount financed.	2500 [PV] [STO]	FIN	**2500.00**
5. Calculate add-on interest.	[×] 8 [%] [×] 3 [=]	FIN	**600.00**
6. Calculate and enter monthly payment.	[+] [RCL] [=]	FIN	**3100.00**
	[÷] 36 [=] [PMT]	FIN	**86.11**
7. Compute monthly nominal interest rate.	[2nd] [%i]	FIN	**1.21**
8. Convert to APR.	[×] 12 [=]	FIN	**14.55**

Your lending institution should quote an APR of 14.55%. (Notice that add-on interest rates often appear to be very low, but the equivalent annual rate is quite high.)

Reference:

Greynolds, Aronofsky, and Frame, *Financial Analysis Using Calculators: Time Value of Money,* pp. 409-413.

Converting APR to Add-On Interest Rates

You borrow $3000 for two years at 14% APR, compounded monthly, to be paid back monthly. What is the equivalent add-on interest rate?

Procedure	Press		Display
1. Clear calculator and mode registers; select two decimal places.	[ON/C] [2nd] [CMR] [FIX] 2		0.00
2. Select financial mode ("FIN" shows in the display).	[2nd] [Mode]	FIN	0.00
3. Calculate and enter number of periods.	2 [×] 12 [=] [N]	FIN	24.00
4. Calculate and enter periodic interest rate.	14 [÷] 12 [=] [%i]	FIN	1.17
5. Enter amount of loan.	3000 [PV]	FIN	3000.00
6. Compute amount of payment.	[2nd] [PMT]	FIN	144.04
7. Reenter payment to nearest cent.*	144.04 [PMT]	FIN	144.04
8. Compute accumulated interest paid on loan.	24 [2nd] [Acc/Bal]	FIN	456.96
9. Divide by number of years and loan amount to calculate add-on rate.	[÷] 2 [÷] 3000 [=]	FIN	0.08
10. Multiply by 100 to calculate add-on rate as a percent.	[×] 100 [=]	FIN	7.62

The equivalent add-on interest rate is 7.62%.

*Although the display in step 6 shows the payment amount rounded to two decimal places, the calculator would use all internal digits (up to 11) for subsequent calculations. For proper results, the payment amount must be rounded to two decimal places and then entered in step 7 because the bank or lending institution would use the rounded value, and not the calculator's internal value, in its calculations.

CHAPTER 7

Finding the Savings That Result from a Down Payment

You need to buy a new refrigerator ($895) and can afford a monthly payment of $50 a month. The finance company charges 18% APR, compounded monthly. How would it affect the loan if you made a $300 down payment, rather than financing the entire purchase?

Procedure	Press		Display
1. Clear calculator and mode registers; select two decimal places.	[ON/C] [STO] [2nd] [CMR] [FIX] 2		**0.00**
2. Select financial mode ("FIN" shows in the display).	[2nd] [Mode]	FIN	**0.00**
A. Find the interest paid without a down payment.			
3. Calculate and enter periodic interest rate.	18 [÷] 12 [=] [%i]	FIN	**1.50**
4. Enter amount of payment.	50 [PMT]	FIN	**50.00**
5. Enter and store purchase price.	895 [PV] [STO]	FIN	**895.00**
6. Compute number of payments needed to pay off loan.	[2nd] [N]	FIN	**21.00**
7. Calculate total amount (principal plus interest) you will pay.	50 [×] 21 [=]	FIN	**1050.00**
8. Subtract purchase price to calculate total amount of interest paid without a down payment. (Leave your calculator on.)	[−] [RCL] [=]	FIN	**155.00**

B. Find the interest paid with a $300 down payment.

Procedure	Press		Display
9. Deduct down payment from purchase price; enter and store new present value.	[RCL] [−] 300 [=] [PV] [STO]	FIN	**595.00**
10. Compute number of payments needed to pay off this loan.	[2nd] [N]	FIN	**13.21**
11. Calculate total amount (number of payments × amount of payment).	[×] 50 [=]	FIN	**660.31**
12. Calculate total interest.	[−] [RCL] [=]	FIN	**65.31**
13. Compare this amount to total interest paid without a down payment (step 8).	[+/−] [+] 155 [=]	FIN	**89.69**

Almost $90 in interest is saved by making the $300 down payment.

CHAPTER 7

Determining the Payment Amount on a Deferred Loan

Julie has borrowed $5000 to be repaid at the end of each month for 24 months with an APR of 13% compounded monthly. What is her monthly payment if she makes the first payment (a) one month or (b) two months after the loan origination date?

Most loan payments are made at the end of the specified period (a month, in this case) and begin one period after the loan is made. Occasionally, however, the first loan payment might be deferred an additional period. If so, the monthly payment amount can be determined as follows:

1. Compute the future value of the original loan amount after one period (steps 7 through 9).
2. Enter the future value as the present value and find the payment amount (steps 10 through 12).

Procedure	Press		Display
1. Clear calculator and mode registers; select two decimal places.	[ON/C] [2nd] [CMR] [FIX] 2		**0.00**
2. Select financial mode ("FIN" shows in the display).	[2nd] [Mode]	FIN	**0.00**
3. Enter number of payment periods.	24 [N]	FIN	**24.00**
4. Calculate and enter periodic interest rate.	13 [÷] 12 [=] [%i]	FIN	**1.08**
5. Enter loan amount.	5000 [PV]	FIN	**5000.00**

Determining the Payment Amount on a Deferred Loan

	Procedure	Press		Display
6.	**Compute payment amount without deferred payment.**	[2nd] [PMT]	FIN	**237.71**
7.	Enter 0 (zero) for payment.	0 [PMT]	FIN	**0.00**
8.	Enter 1 (one) for number of periods.	1 [N]	FIN	**1.00**
9.	Compute loan value at end of first month.	[2nd] [FV]	FIN	**5054.17**
10.	Enter loan value from step 9 as present value.	[PV]	FIN	**5054.17**
11.	Enter number of payment periods.	24 [N]	FIN	**24.00**
12.	**Compute payment with deferred payments.**	[2nd] [PMT]	FIN	**240.28**

If Julie defers her first payment for two months rather than the usual one month, her monthly payments will be $240.28 instead of $237.71.

CHAPTER 7

Amortizing a Loan with the Rule of 78's

You are planning to borrow $2500 at 11.5% APR, compounded monthly. You will make 24 monthly payments of $117.10 each. With the Rule of 78's method,* prepare an amortization schedule for the first seven payments and find the amount required to pay off the loan after the seventh payment.

Loans amortized by the Rule of 78's method will reflect principal and interest amounts which differ from loans computed by the actuarial or compound interest amortization method. The Rule of 78's method is similar to the sum-of-the-years'-digits depreciation method, except here you amortize the total interest on the loan.

Procedure	Press	Display
1. Clear calculator and select two decimal places.	[ON/C] [STO] [FIX] 2	0.00
2. Calculate and store sum of digits for number of payments.*	24 [+] 1 [×] 24 [÷] 2 [=] [STO]	300.00
3. Calculate total amount of interest paid.	24 [×] 117.10 [−] 2500 [=]	310.40
4. Divide by sum of digits and store result.	[÷] [RCL] [=] [STO]	1.03
5. Enter last payment number and set up constant to calculate interest portion of first payment* (and other payments); store result.	24 [×] [K] [RCL] [=] [STO]	24.83

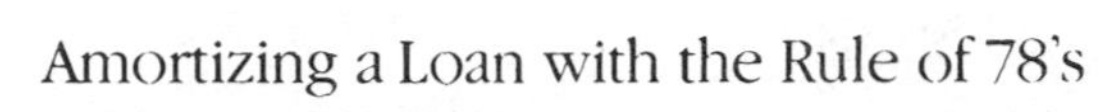

Amortizing a Loan with the Rule of 78's

	Procedure	Press	Display
6.	**Calculate interest portion of other payments; * add values in memory.**		
a.	Second payment.	23 [=] [SUM]	**23.80**
b.	Third payment.	22 [=] [SUM]	**22.76**
c.	Fourth payment.	21 [=] [SUM]	**21.73**
d.	Fifth payment.	20 [=] [SUM]	**20.69**
e.	Sixth payment.	19 [=] [SUM]	**19.66**
f.	Seventh payment.	18 [=] [SUM]	**18.62**
7.	Recall total amount of interest paid.	[RCL]	**152.10**
8.	Enter number of payments and multiply by amount of payment.	7 [×] 117.10 [=]	**819.70**
9.	Subtract result from amount of loan.	[+/-] [+] 2500 [=]	**1680.30**
10.	**Add result to total amount of interest paid to calculate amount required to pay off loan immediately after seventh payment.**	[+] [RCL] [=]	**1832.40**

*See *Appendix A* for the formula.

CHAPTER 7

Finding the Payoff Amount on a Loan with the Rule of 78's

We are using the same values as in the previous example, so that you can compare the procedures. You are planning to borrow $2500 at 11.5% APR, compounded monthly. You will make 24 monthly payments of $117.10 each. By the Rule of 78's method, find the rebate, the amount of interest paid, and the payoff amount after seven payments, without preparing an amortization schedule.

The solution can be found as follows:

1. Calculate the total interest due on the original loan (step 2).
2. Use the Rule of 78's* to compute the rebate received for early payoff (steps 3 through 6).
3. Subtract the rebate from the interest due on the original loan to find the amount of interest paid (step 7).
4. Calculate the payoff amount (steps 8 through 10) by subtracting the total amount of loan payments for the specified period from the total amount due (interest + loan amount).

Procedure	Press	Display
1. Clear calculator and select two decimal places.	[ON/C] [STO] [FIX] 2	**0.00**
2. Calculate total amount of interest on loan (number of payments × payment amount − loan amount).	24 [×] 117.10 [−] 2500 [=]	**310.40**
3. Subtract number of last payment from total number of payments to calculate number of remaining payments.	24 [−] 7 [=] [STO]	**17.00**
4. Add 1 (one) to displayed value and multiply by number of remaining payments (step 3).	[+] 1 [×] [RCL] [=]	**306.00**

Finding the Payoff Amount on a Loan with the Rule of 78's

Procedure	Press	Display
5. Divide by total number of payments and by number of payments plus 1; store result.	[÷] 24 [÷] 25 [=] [STO]	**0.51**
6. Multiply interest due on loan (step 2) by amount in memory to calculate rebate.	310.40 [×] [RCL] [=]	**158.30**
7. Subtract displayed value (rebate) from interest on loan (step 2) to calculate amount of interest paid.	[+/−] [+] 310.40 [=]	**152.10**
8. Add displayed value to amount of loan to calculate total amount paid; store result.	[+] 2500 [=] [STO]	**2652.10**
9. Multiply number of payments made by payment amount.	7 [×] 117.10 [=]	**819.70**
10. Subtract result from total amount paid (step 8) to calculate payoff amount.	[+/−] [+] [RCL] [=]	**1832.40**

The rebate is $158.30, and you would pay $152.10 in interest. Immediately following the seventh payment, the payoff amount is $1,832.40.

*See *Appendix A* for the formula.

Reference:

Greynolds, Aronofsky, and Frame, *Financial Analysis Using Calculators: Time Value of Money,* pp. 409-413.

CHAPTER 7

U.S. Method for Amortizing Loans with Compound Interest

A company is buying a machine and will pay off the loan in six monthly installments. The machine costs $18,000, and the APR on the loan is 11.5%, compounded monthly. How much is the payment; what will the principal, interest, and remaining balance be after the third payment; and what is the complete amortization schedule?

Procedure	Press		Display
1. Clear calculator and mode registers; select two decimal places.	ON/C 2nd CMR FIX 2		0.00
2. Select financial mode ("FIN" shows in the display).	2nd Mode	FIN	0.00
3. Enter number of periods.	6 N	FIN	6.00
4. Calculate and enter monthly interest rate.	11.5 ÷ 12 = %i	FIN	0.96
5. Enter amount of loan.	18000 PV	FIN	18000.00
6. Compute payment amount.	2nd PMT	FIN	**3101.42**
7. Enter amount of payment rounded to nearest cent.*	3101.42 PMT	FIN	3101.42
8. Compute number of periods.	2nd N	FIN	6.00
9. Enter 3rd period and compute principal.	3 2nd P/I	FIN	**2985.33**
10. Display interest.	x:y	FIN	**116.09**
11. Enter 3rd period and compute remaining balance.	3 2nd Acc/Bal x:y	FIN	**9128.76**
12. Find values for 1st period.			
a. Compute principal.	1 2nd P/I	FIN	**2928.92**
b. Display interest.	x:y	FIN	**172.50**
c. Compute remaining balance.	1 2nd Acc/Bal x:y	FIN	**15071.08**

Procedure	Press		Display
13. Find values for 2nd period.			
a. Compute principal.	2 [2nd] [P/I]	FIN	**2956.99**
b. Display interest.	[x:y]	FIN	**144.43**
c. Compute remaining balance.	2 [2nd] [Acc/Bal] [x:y]	FIN	**12114.09**
14. Find values for 4th period.			
a. Compute principal.	4 [2nd] [P/I]	FIN	**3013.94**
b. Display interest.	[x:y]	FIN	**87.48**
c. Compute remaining balance.	4 [2nd] [Acc/Bal] [x:y]	FIN	**6114.83**
15. Find values for 5th period.			
a. Compute principal.	5 [2nd] [P/I]	FIN	**3042.82**
b. Display interest.	[x:y]	FIN	**58.60**
c. Compute remaining balance.	5 [2nd] [Acc/Bal] [x:y]	FIN	**3072.01**
16. Find values for 6th period.			
a. Compute principal.	6 [2nd] [P/I]	FIN	**3071.98**
b. Display interest.	[x:y]	FIN	**29.44**
c. Compute remaining balance.	6 [2nd] [Acc/Bal] [x:y]	FIN	**0.03**

Since the payment amount entered in step 7 was rounded to two decimal places, you have a $0.03 remaining balance rather than a zero balance.

*Although the display in step 6 shows the payment amount rounded to two decimal places, the calculator would use all internal digits (up to 11) for subsequent calculations. For proper results, the payment amount must be rounded to two decimal places and then entered in step 7 because the bank or lending institution would use the rounded value, and not the calculator's internal value, in its calculations.

CHAPTER 7

European Method for Amortizing Loans with Compound Interest

We are using the same values as in the previous example, so that you can compare the results. A company is taking out a loan for $18,000, which it will repay in six monthly installments. The effective annual interest rate is 11.5%, compounded monthly. What is the monthly payment amount; what will be the interest, principal, and remaining balance after the third payment; and what is the complete amortization schedule?

The European or Effective Interest Method of computing a loan amortization schedule differs only in the way the periodic interest is determined. Annual interest is stated as an effective, rather than nominal, rate; therefore, it is incorrect to divide the annual rate by the number of compounding periods per year to find the periodic compounding rate. Instead, the periodic rate must be calculated as illustrated here.

Procedure	Press		Display
1. Clear calculator and mode registers; select floating decimal point.	[ON/C] [2nd] [CMR] [FIX] 8		**0**
2. Select financial mode ("FIN" shows in the display).	[2nd] [Mode]	FIN	**0**
3. Convert effective interest rate to periodic rate.			
a. Enter number of payments per year.	12 [N]	FIN	**12**
b. Enter 1 (one) as present value.	1 [PV]	FIN	**1**
c. Add 1 (one) to effective interest rate and enter as future value.	1 [+] 11.5 [%] [=] [FV]	FIN	**1.115**
d. Compute periodic effective interest rate.	[2nd] [%i]	FIN	**0.9112467**

The periodic interest rate is 0.911%.

European Method for Amortizing Loans with Compound Interest

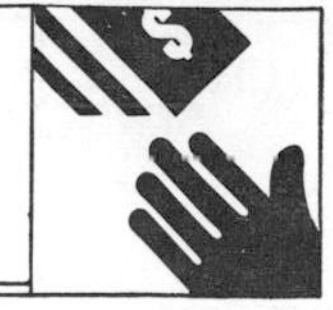

Procedure	Press		Display
4. Select two decimal places. (Only the display is rounded; all internal digits – up to 11 – are retained.)	[FIX] 2	FIN	**0.91**
5. Enter number of payments.	6 [N]	FIN	**6.00**
6. Enter loan amount.	18000 [PV]	FIN	**18000.00**
7. Compute periodic loan payment.	[2nd] [PMT]	FIN	**3096.40**
8. Reenter amount of payment.*	3096.40 [PMT]	FIN	**3096.40**
9. Compute number of periods.	[2nd] [N]	FIN	**6.00**
10. Enter 3rd period and compute principal.	3 [2nd] [P/I]	FIN	**2986.06**
11. Display interest.	[x:y]	FIN	**110.34**
12. Enter 3rd period and compute remaining balance.	3 [2nd] [Acc/Bal] [x:y]	FIN	**9122.47**
13. Find values for 1st period.			
a. Compute principal.	1 [2nd] [P/I]	FIN	**2932.38**
b. Display interest.	[x:y]	FIN	**164.02**
c. Compute remaining balance.	1 [2nd] [Acc/Bal] [x:y]	FIN	**15067.62**
14. Find values for 2nd period.			
a. Compute principal.	2 [2nd] [P/I]	FIN	**2959.10**
b. Display interest.	[x:y]	FIN	**137.30**
c. Compute remaining balance.	2 [2nd] [Acc/Bal] [x:y]	FIN	**12108.53**

(continued on next page)

Procedure	Press		Display
15. Find values for 4th period.			
a. Compute principal.	4 [2nd] [P/I]	FIN	**3013.27**
b. Display interest.	[x:y]	FIN	**83.13**
c. Compute remaining balance.	4 [2nd] [Acc/Bal] [x:y]	FIN	**6109.19**
16. Find values for 5th period.			
a. Compute principal.	5 [2nd] [P/I]	FIN	**3040.73**
b. Display interest.	[x:y]	FIN	**55.67**
c. Compute remaining balance.	5 [2nd] [Acc/Bal] [x:y]	FIN	**3068.46**
17. Find values for 6th period.			
a. Compute principal.	6 [2nd] [P/I]	FIN	**3068.44**
b. Display interest.	[x:y]	FIN	**27.96**
c. Compute remaining balance.	6 [2nd] [Acc/Bal] [x:y]	FIN	**0.03**

*Although the display in step 7 shows the payment amount rounded to two decimal places, the calculator would use all internal digits (up to 11) for subsequent calculations. For proper results, the payment amount must be rounded to two decimal places and then entered in step 8 because the bank or lending institution would use the rounded value, and not the calculator's internal value, in its calculations.

Determining an Installment Plan Schedule When the Principal Payment Is Fixed

A lounge chair is priced at $120. If you decide to make the purchase, the store will apply its six-month installment plan at 1 1/2% interest on the unpaid balance each month. This means that the unpaid balance will decrease by $120 ÷ 6 each month, or $20. Your unpaid balance will be $120 for the first month, $100 for the second month, $80 for the third month, etc. If payments are made at the end of each month, what will your monthly payment be each month including all interest charges?

Procedure	Press	Display
1. Clear calculator and select two decimal places.	[ON/C] [STO] [FIX] 2	0.00
2. Calculate first month's interest (unpaid balance × monthly interest rate).	120 [×] 1.5 [%] [=]	1.80
3. Calculate first month's payment (interest + monthly payment).	[+] 20 [STO] [=]	**21.80**
4. Calculate second month's payment.	100 [×] 1.5 [%] [+] [RCL] [=]	**21.50**
5. Calculate third month's payment.	80 [×] 1.5 [%] [+] [RCL] [=]	**21.20**
6. Calculate fourth month's payment.	60 [×] 1.5 [%] [+] [RCL] [=]	**20.90**
7. Calculate fifth month's payment.	40 [×] 1.5 [%] [+] [RCL] [=]	**20.60**
8. Calculate final payment.	20 [×] 1.5 [%] [+] [RCL] [=]	**20.30**

CHAPTER

8 SAVINGS

The amount of interest earned on a savings account is determined by several factors, including the annual interest rate and the method of compounding. Banks and savings institutions can compound interest quarterly, weekly, daily, or continuously. With your calculator you can quickly evaluate various rates and compounding periods to determine the best savings institution for you.

In some cases, you might select a savings account where the number of compounding periods per year does not equal the number of deposits (payments) you make each year. Or you might want to compare a discrete interest rate (uses a specified period for compounding, such as weekly) with a continuous interest rate. The conversion routines necessary for comparing these interest situations on the basis of the same time period are included here. *Appendix A* lists the conversion formulas.

The examples in this chapter assume that the savings institution pays interest for partial compounding periods. In other words, if the institution pays interest weekly and you deposit money in the middle of the week, you receive interest for the remainder of the week.

When you are selecting a savings institution, keep in mind that, if the annual interest rates are equal, the account with the largest number of compounding periods per year will earn the most interest. Also, savings institutions often quote the interest rate rounded to the nearest 1/4%. When the quoted rate is used in calculations, the answer may differ slightly from the amount calculated by the savings institution.

Determining the Time Needed to Earn a Specified Amount

You plan to deposit $1200 in a savings account and withdraw the money when it equals $3600. How long will the money remain in the account if the annual interest rate is 6.5% compounded quarterly?

Procedure	Press		Display
1. Clear calculator and mode registers; select two decimal places.	[ON/C] [2nd] [CMR] [FIX] 2		**0.00**
2. Select financial mode ("FIN" shows in the display).	[2nd] [Mode]	FIN	**0.00**
3. Calculate and enter periodic interest rate.	6.5 [÷] 4 [=] [%i]	FIN	**1.63**
4. Enter amount of deposit or investment.	1200 [PV]	FIN	**1200.00**
5. Enter future value.	3600 [FV]	FIN	**3600.00**
6. Compute number of periods.	[2nd] [N]	FIN	**68.15**
7. Divide by number of periods per year to calculate number of years.	[÷] 4 [=]	FIN	**17.04**

You must invest the money for 17.04 years with quarterly compounding.

CHAPTER 8

Finding the Future Value of a Single Deposit

You have deposited $1800 in a savings account, and you plan to leave the money there for seven years. How much money will you have if the annual interest rate is 5.5% (a) compounded monthly or (b) compounded continuously?

A. Finding the value of a deposit with monthly compounding.

Procedure	Press		Display
1. Clear calculator and mode registers; select two decimal places.	[ON/C] [2nd] [CMR] [FIX] 2		**0.00**
2. Select financial mode ("FIN" shows in the display).	[2nd] [Mode]	FIN	**0.00**
3. Calculate and enter number of periods (months).	7 [×] 12 [=] [N]	FIN	**84.00**
4. Calculate and enter periodic (monthly) interest rate.	5.5 [÷] 12 [=] [%i]	FIN	**0.46**
5. Enter amount of deposit.	1800 [PV]	FIN	**1800.00**
6. Compute future value.	[2nd] [FV]	FIN	**2642.98**

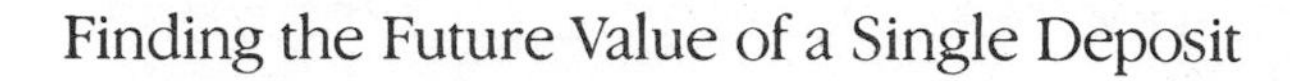

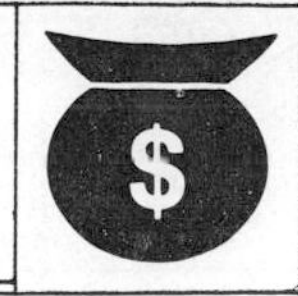

B. Finding the value of a deposit with continuous compounding.

In this case, the continuous interest rate must be converted to an equivalent discrete rate before computing the future value.

Procedure	Press		Display
1. Clear calculator and mode registers; select two decimal places.	[ON/C] [2nd] [CMR] [FIX] 2		0.00
2. Select financial mode ("FIN" shows in the display).	[2nd] [Mode]	FIN	0.00
3. Enter number of years.	7 [N]	FIN	7.00
4. Convert continuous rate to equivalent discrete rate.*			
a. Enter continuous rate.	5.5 [%]	FIN	0.06
b. Calculate equivalent discrete rate.	[2nd] [eˣ] [−] 1 [=]	FIN	0.06
c. Convert discrete rate to percent and enter as %i.	[×] 100 [=] [%i]	FIN	5.65
7. Enter amount of deposit.	1800 [PV]	FIN	1800.00
8. Compute future value.	[2nd] [FV]	FIN	2645.31

In seven years, you will have $2,642.98 if interest is compounded monthly or $2,645.31 if interest is compounded continuously.

*See *Appendix A* for the formula.

CHAPTER **8**

How Much Should You Deposit Today to Have a Specified Amount in the Future?

You are planning to travel to Europe in two years. How much should you invest today to have $3500 for your trip with an annual interest rate of 7.5% (a) compounded daily or (b) compounded continuously? (Use a 365-day year.)

A. Finding the deposit amount with daily compounding.

Procedure	Press		Display
1. Clear calculator and mode registers; select two decimal places.	[ON/C] [2nd] [CMR] [FIX] 2		**0.00**
2. Select financial mode ("FIN" shows in the display).	[2nd] [Mode]	FIN	**0.00**
3. Calculate and enter number of periods (days).	2 [×] 365 [=] [N]	FIN	**730.00**
4. Calculate and enter periodic (daily) interest rate.	7.5 [÷] 365 [=] [%i]	FIN	**0.02**
5. Enter future value.	3500 [FV]	FIN	**3500.00**
6. Compute amount of deposit.	[2nd] [PV]	FIN	**3012.52**

B. Finding the deposit amount with continuous compounding.

Procedure	Press		Display
1. Clear calculator and mode registers; select two decimal places.	[ON/C] [2nd] [CMR] [FIX] 2		**0.00**
2. Select financial mode ("FIN" shows in the display).	[2nd] [Mode]	FIN	**0.00**
3. Enter number of years.	2 [N]	FIN	**2.00**
4. Convert continuous rate to equivalent discrete rate.*			
a. Enter continuous interest rate.	7.5 [%]	FIN	**0.08**
b. Calculate equivalent discrete rate.	[2nd] [e^x] [−] 1 [=]	FIN	**0.08**
c. Convert discrete rate to percent and enter as %i.	[×] 100 [=] [%i]	FIN	**7.79**
7. Enter future value.	3500 [FV]	FIN	**3500.00**
8. Compute amount of deposit.	[2nd] [PV]	FIN	**3012.48**

To have $3500 at the end of two years, you need to deposit $3012.52 if interest is compounded daily or $3012.48 if interest is compounded continuously. Notice that there is very little difference between the amount of the deposit with daily compounding and the amount necessary with continuous compounding.

*See *Appendix A* for the formula.

Determining the Interest Rate Required for Your Money to Grow to a Certain Amount

You have an opportunity to invest $1700 today and receive $2800 at the end of five years. What is the interest rate if compounding occurs (a) monthly or (b) continuously?

A. Finding the interest rate with monthly compounding.

Procedure	Press		Display
1. Clear calculator and mode registers; select two decimal places.	ON/C 2nd CMR FIX 2		**0.00**
2. Select financial mode ("FIN" shows in the display).	2nd Mode	FIN	**0.00**
3. Calculate and enter number of periods.	5 × 12 = N	FIN	**60.00**
4. Enter amount of investment or deposit.	1700 PV	FIN	**1700.00**
5. Enter future value.	2800 FV	FIN	**2800.00**
6. Compute periodic interest rate.	2nd %i	FIN	**0.84**
7. Multiply by number of compounding periods per year to calculate annual interest rate.	× 12 =	FIN	**10.02**

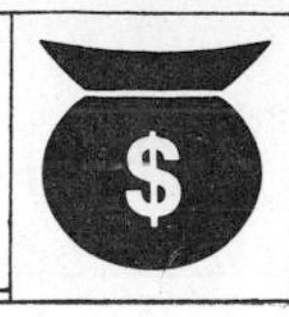

B. Finding the interest rate with continuous compounding.

Procedure	Press		Display
1. Clear calculator and mode registers; select two decimal places.	[ON/C] [2nd] [CMR] [FIX] 2		**0.00**
2. Select financial mode ("FIN" shows in the display).	[2nd] [Mode]	FIN	**0.00**
3. Enter number of years.	5 [N]	FIN	**5.00**
4. Enter amount of investment or deposit.	1700 [PV]	FIN	**1700.00**
5. Enter future value.	2800 [FV]	FIN	**2800.00**
6. Compute discrete interest rate compounded at end of each year.	[2nd] [%i]	FIN	**10.49**
7. Convert discrete rate to equivalent continuous rate.*			
a. Convert percent to decimal.	[%]	FIN	**0.10**
b. Calculate annual continuous rate as a decimal.	[+] 1 [=] [2nd] [lnx]	FIN	**0.10**
c. Convert to percent.	[×] 100 [=]	FIN	**9.98**

The annual interest rate is 10.02% with monthly compounding and 9.98% with continuous compounding.

*See *Appendix A* for the formula.

CHAPTER 8

Determining How Much Your Savings Will Be Worth with a Series of Equal Deposits

You plan to deposit $300 in a savings account at the beginning of each month. How much will you have in the account after four years if the annual interest rate is 6 1/4% (a) compounded monthly, (b) compounded quarterly, or (c) compounded continuously?

A. Finding the future value when the number of compounding periods equals the number of payment periods.

Procedure	Press		Display
1. Clear calculator and mode registers; select two decimal places.	[ON/C] [2nd] [CMR] [FIX] 2		0.00
2. Select financial mode ("FIN" shows in the display).	[2nd] [Mode]	FIN	0.00
3. Calculate and enter number of periods.	4 [×] 12 [=] [N]	FIN	48.00
4. Calculate and enter periodic interest rate.	6.25 [÷] 12 [=] [%i]	FIN	0.52
5. Enter amount of deposit.	300 [PMT]	FIN	300.00
6. Compute future value.	[DUE] [FV]	FIN	**16396.85**

B. Finding the future value when the number of compounding periods does not equal the number of payment periods.

In this case, the interest rate per compounding period must be converted to the rate per payment period before you compute the future value. See "Finding the Future Value of an Annuity Where Compounding Periods and Payment Periods Are Not Equal" in Chapter 3.

Determining How Much Your Savings Will Be Worth with a Series of Equal Deposits

Procedure	Press		Display
1. Clear calculator and mode registers; select two decimal places.	[ON/C] [2nd] [CMR] [FIX] 2		0.00
2. Select financial mode ("FIN" shows in the display).	[2nd] [Mode]	FIN	0.00
3. Convert interest rate per compounding period to rate per payment period.			
a. Enter number of compounding periods per year.	4 [N]	FIN	4.00
b. Calculate and enter interest rate per compounding period.	6.25 [÷] 4 [=] [%i]	FIN	1.56
c. Enter (1) one for present value.	1 [PV]	FIN	1.00
d. Compute future value.	[2nd] [FV]	FIN	1.06
e. Enter number of payment periods per year.	12 [N]	FIN	12.00
f. Compute interest rate per payment period.	[2nd] [%i]	FIN	0.52
4. Calculate and enter number of deposits.	4 [×] 12 [=] [N]	FIN	48.00
5. Enter amount of deposit.	300 [PMT]	FIN	300.00
6. Compute future value.	[DUE] [FV]	FIN	16385.67

(continued on next page)

C. Finding the future value with continuous compounding.

Procedure	Press		Display
1. Clear calculator and mode registers; select two decimal places.	[ON/C] [2nd] [CMR] [FIX] 2		0.00
2. Select financial mode ("FIN" shows in the display).	[2nd] [Mode]	FIN	0.00
3. Calculate and enter number of periods.	4 [×] 12 [=] [N]	FIN	48.00
4. Convert continuous rate to equivalent discrete rate.*			
a. Divide annual rate by number of payments per year.	6.25 [%] [÷] 12 [=]	FIN	0.01
b. Calculate equivalent discrete rate.	[2nd] [e^x] [−] 1 [=]	FIN	0.01
c. Convert discrete rate to percent and enter as %i.	[×] 100 [=] [%i]	FIN	0.52
5. Enter amount of deposit.	300 [PMT]	FIN	300.00
6. Compute future value.	[DUE] [FV]	FIN	**16402.50**

As you would expect, the account is worth the most ($16,402.50) with continuous compounding, and the amount ($16,396.85) in the account with monthly compounding exceeds the amount ($16,385.67) with quarterly compounding.

*See *Appendix A* for the formula.

Finding the Amount of Regular Deposits Necessary to Have a Specified Amount in the Future

You want to deposit a regular amount in a savings account at the beginning of each month so that you will have $25,000 in ten years. How much should you deposit if the annual interest rate is 7% compounded monthly?

Procedure	Press		Display
1. Clear calculator and mode registers; select two decimal places.	[ON/C] [2nd] [CMR] [FIX] 2		0.00
2. Select financial mode ("FIN" shows in the display).	[2nd] [Mode]	FIN	0.00
3. Calculate and enter number of deposits.	10 [×] 12 [=] [N]	FIN	120.00
4. Calculate and enter periodic interest rate.	7 [÷] 12 [=] [%i]	FIN	0.58
5. Enter future value.	25000 [FV]	FIN	25000.00
6. Compute payment amount.	[DUE] [PMT]	FIN	**143.60**

If the annual interest rate is 7% compounded monthly, you need to make monthly deposits of $143.60.

The monthly deposit amount would be $143.47 with weekly compounding and $143.44 with continuous compounding. To calculate either of these, follow the method as explained in the example "Determining How Much Your Savings Will Be Worth with a Series of Equal Deposits" in this chapter. Convert the interest rate, enter the other two known values ([N] and [FV]), and solve for the unknown value ([DUE] [PMT]). For an explanation of the interest rate conversion, see "Finding the Future Value of an Annuity Where Compounding Periods and Payment Periods Are Not Equal" in Chapter 3.

CHAPTER 8

Determining the Interest Rate on a Series of Regular Deposits

At the beginning of each month for five years, you deposited $500 in a savings account and you now have $37,000. What was the average annual interest rate with (a) monthly compounding, (b) quarterly compounding, or (c) continuous compounding?

A. Finding the interest rate when the number of compounding periods equals the number of payment periods.

	Procedure	Press		Display
1.	Clear calculator and mode registers; select two decimal places.	[ON/C] [2nd] [CMR] [FIX] 2		**0.00**
2.	Select financial mode ("FIN" shows in the display).	[2nd] [Mode]	FIN	**0.00**
3.	Calculate and enter number of deposits.	5 [×] 12 [=] [N]	FIN	**60.00**
4.	Enter amount of deposits.	500 [PMT]	FIN	**500.00**
5.	Enter future value.	37000 [FV]	FIN	**37000.00**
6.	Compute interest rate per compounding period.	[DUE] [%i]	FIN	**0.67**
7.	**Multiply by number of periods per year to calculate annual interest rate.**	[×] 12 [=]	FIN	**8.02**

B. Finding the interest rate when the number of compounding periods does not equal the number of payment periods.

To solve the problem, compute the interest rate per payment period and convert it to the equivalent rate per compounding period. See "Determining the Interest Rate Where Compounding Periods and Payment Periods Are Not Equal" in Chapter 3.

Determining the Interest Rate on a Series of Regular Deposits

Procedure	Press		Display
1. Clear calculator and mode registers; select two decimal places.	[ON/C] [2nd] [CMR] [FIX] 2		0.00
2. Select financial mode ("FIN" shows in the display).	[2nd] [Mode]	FIN	0.00
3. Calculate and enter number of deposits.	5 [×] 12 [=] [N]	FIN	60.00
4. Enter amount of deposit.	500 [PMT]	FIN	500.00
5. Enter future value.	37000 [FV]	FIN	37000.00
6. Compute interest rate per payment period.	[DUE] [%i]	FIN	0.67
7. Convert rate per payment period to rate per compounding period.			
a. Enter 0 (zero) for payment.	0 [PMT]	FIN	0.00
b. Enter number of payments per year.	12 [N]	FIN	12.00
c. Enter 1 (one) for present value.	1 [PV]	FIN	1.00
d. Compute future value.	[2nd] [FV]	FIN	1.08
e. Enter number of compounding periods per year.	4 [N]	FIN	4.00
f. Compute interest rate per compounding period.	[2nd] [%i]	FIN	2.02
8. Multiply by number of compounding periods per year to calculate annual interest rate.	[×] 4 [=]	FIN	8.07

(continued on next page)

C. Finding the interest rate with continuous compounding.

Procedure	Press		Display
1. Clear calculator and mode registers; select two decimal places.	[ON/C] [2nd] [CMR] [FIX] 2		**0.00**
2. Select financial mode ("FIN" shows in the display).	[2nd] [Mode]	FIN	**0.00**
3. Calculate and enter number of deposits.	5 [×] 12 [=] [N]	FIN	**60.00**
4. Enter amount of deposits.	500 [PMT]	FIN	**500.00**
5. Enter future value.	37000 [FV]	FIN	**37000.00**
6. Compute discrete interest rate per payment period.	[DUE] [%i]	FIN	**0.67**
7. Convert discrete rate to equivalent continuous rate.*			
a. Convert percent to decimal.	[%]	FIN	**0.01**
b. Calculate periodic continuous rate as a decimal.	[+] 1 [=] [2nd] [lnx]	FIN	**0.01**
c. Multiply by number of payments per year to calculate annual continuous rate.	[×] 12 [=]	FIN	**0.08**
d. Multiply by 100 to find rate as percent.	[×] 100 [=]	FIN	**7.99**

The annual interest rate is 8.02% with monthly compounding, 8.07% with quarterly compounding, and 7.99% with continuous compounding.

*See *Appendix A* for the formula.

How Long Will It Take You to Save a Certain Amount If You Make Monthly Deposits?

You are saving to buy a new car which sells for $6500, and you can deposit $275 in your savings account at the beginning of each month. How long will it take to save the money if the annual interest rate is 5.75% compounded monthly?

Procedure	Press		Display
1. Clear calculator and mode registers; select two decimal places.	[ON/C] [2nd] [CMR] [FIX] 2		0.00
2. Select financial mode ("FIN" shows in the display).	[2nd] [Mode]	FIN	0.00
3. Calculate and enter periodic interest rate.	5.75 [÷] 12 [=] [%i]	FIN	0.48
4. Enter amount of deposit.	275 [PMT]	FIN	275.00
5. Enter future value.	6500 [FV]	FIN	6500.00
6. Compute number of payments.	[DUE] [N]	FIN	**22.34**

You would need to make 23 payments with an annual interest rate of 5.75% compounded monthly to have at least $6500.

With daily or continuous compounding, 23 payments would also be required. To verify this, follow the procedure given in the example "Determining How Much Your Savings Will Be Worth with a Series of Equal Deposits" in this chapter. Convert the interest rate, enter the other two known values ([PMT] and [FV]), and solve for the unknown value ([DUE] [N]). For an explanation of the interest rate conversion, see "Finding the Future Value of an Annuity Where Compounding Periods and Payment Periods Are Not Equal" in Chapter 3.

CHAPTER 8

Finding the Future Value of an Account with a Beginning Balance and a Series of Regular Payments

You will have $5000 in your savings account at the beginning of next month. At that time, you plan to start depositing $150 at the beginning of each month. How much money will you have in the account after 22 months if the annual interest rate is 6.5% compounded (a) monthly, (b) quarterly, or (c) continuously?

The future value of the account is the sum of the future value of the initial deposit ($5000) and the future value of the periodic (monthly) deposits.

A. Finding the future value when the number of compounding periods equals the number of payment periods.

Procedure	Press		Display
1. Clear calculator and mode registers; select two decimal places.	[ON/C] [STO] [2nd] [CMR] [FIX] 2		**0.00**
2. Select financial mode ("FIN" shows in the display).	[2nd] [Mode]	FIN	**0.00**
3. Enter number of deposits.	22 [N]	FIN	**22.00**
4. Calculate and enter periodic interest rate.	6.5 [÷] 12 [=] [%i]	FIN	**0.54**
5. Enter beginning balance of account.	5000 [PV]	FIN	**5000.00**
6. Compute and store future value of beginning balance.	[2nd] [FV] [STO]	FIN	**5630.98**
7. Enter amount of deposit.	150 [PMT]	FIN	**150.00**
8. Compute future value of regular deposits and add to memory.	[DUE] [FV] [SUM]	FIN	**3513.57**
9. Recall total future value.	[RCL]	FIN	**9144.55**

B. Finding the future value when the number of compounding periods does not equal the number of payment periods.

Finding the Future Value of an Account with a Beginning Balance and a Series of Regular Payments

	Procedure	Press		Display
1.	Clear calculator and mode registers; select two decimal places.	[ON/C] [STO] [2nd] [CMR] [FIX] 2		**0.00**
2.	Select financial mode ("FIN" shows in the display).	[2nd] [Mode]	FIN	**0.00**
3.	**Convert rate per compounding period to rate per payment period.**			
a.	Enter number of compounding periods per year.	4 [N]	FIN	**4.00**
b.	Calculate and enter interest rate per compounding period.	6.5 [÷] 4 [=] [%i]	FIN	**1.63**
c.	Enter 1 (one) for present value.	1 [PV]	FIN	**1.00**
d.	Compute future value.	[2nd] [FV]	FIN	**1.07**
e.	Enter number of payment periods per year.	12 [N]	FIN	**12.00**
f.	Compute interest rate per payment period.	[2nd] [%i]	FIN	**0.54**
4.	Enter number of deposits.	22 [N]	FIN	**22.00**
5.	Enter amount of beginning balance.	5000 [PV]	FIN	**5000.00**
6.	Compute and store future value of beginning balance.	[2nd] [FV] [STO]	FIN	**5627.40**
7.	Enter amount of regular deposit.	150 [PMT]	FIN	**150.00**
8.	Compute future value of regular deposits and add to memory.	[DUE] [FV] [SUM]	FIN	**3512.38**
9.	**Recall total future value.**	[RCL]	FIN	**9139.78**

(continued on next page)

C. Finding the future value with continuous compounding.

Procedure	Press		Display
1. Clear calculator and mode registers; select two decimal places.	ON/C STO 2nd CMR FIX 2		**0.00**
2. Select financial mode ("FIN" shows in the display).	2nd Mode	FIN	**0.00**
3. Enter number of deposits.	22 N	FIN	**22.00**
4. Convert continuous rate to equivalent discrete rate.*			
a. Divide continuous rate by number of payments per year.	6.5 % ÷ 12 =	FIN	**0.01**
b. Calculate equivalent discrete rate.	2nd eˣ − 1 =	FIN	**0.01**
c. Convert discrete rate to percent and enter as %i.	× 100 = %i	FIN	**0.54**
5. Enter amount of beginning balance.	5000 PV	FIN	**5000.00**
6. Compute and store future value of beginning balance.	2nd FV STO	FIN	**5632.79**
7. Enter amount of regular deposit.	150 PMT	FIN	**150.00**
8. Compute future value of regular payments and add to memory.	DUE FV SUM	FIN	**3514.17**
9. Recall total future value.	RCL	FIN	**9146.96**

After 22 months, you will have $9144.55 with monthly compounding, $9139.78 with quarterly compounding, or $9146.96 with continuous compounding.

*See *Appendix A* for the formula.

Finding the Payment Amount on a Account with a Beginning Balance and a Specified Future Value

Your savings account balance is $10,000 at the beginning of the month, and you want to have $16,000 at the end of three years. How much should you deposit at the beginning of each month if the annual interest rate is 7.75% compounded monthly?

The general solution procedure is:

1. Compute the future value of the beginning balance (steps 3 through 6).
2. Subtract the result from the total desired future value, and enter the new value as the future value (step 7).
3. Compute the payment amount (step 8).

Procedure	Press		Display
1. Clear calculator and mode registers; select two decimal places.	[ON/C] [2nd] [CMR] [FIX] 2		0.00
2. Select financial mode ("FIN" shows in the display).	[2nd] [Mode]	FIN	0.00
3. Calculate and enter number of deposits.	3 [×] 12 [=] [N]	FIN	36.00
4. Calculate and enter periodic interest rate.	7.75 [÷] 12 [=] [%i]	FIN	0.65
5. Enter amount of beginning balance.	10000 [PV]	FIN	10000.00
6. Compute future value of beginning balance.	[2nd] [FV]	FIN	12608.08
7. Subtract from total future value and enter result.	[+/-] [+] 16000 [=] [FV]	FIN	3391.92
8. Compute payment.	[DUE] [PMT]	FIN	**83.45**

With an annual interest rate of 7.75% compounded monthly, you need to make monthly deposits of $83.45.

The payment amount would be $83.25 weekly and $83.19 with continuous compounding. Follow the procedure in "Finding the Future Value of an Account with a Beginning Balance and a Series of Regular Payments" in this chapter to convert the interest rate, and enter the other two known values ([N] and [PV]). Next, find the future value (steps 6 and 7 above) and then solve for the unknown value ([DUE] [PMT]).

CHAPTER 8	Determining the Interest Rate on an Account with a Beginning Balance and a Series of Regular Payments

At the beginning of this month, your savings account had a balance of $5000 and you deposited $75. Assume that you continue to deposit $75 at the beginning of each month for 30 months and that you want to save a total of $8300. What is the required annual interest rate with (a) monthly compounding, (b) weekly compounding, or (c) continuous compounding?

Since the annuity equation cannot directly solve for the interest rate, the solution must be found by a repetitive, trial-and-error process known as an iteration. See steps 4 through 14.

A. Finding the interest rate when the number of compounding periods equals the number of payment periods.

Procedure	Press		Display
1. Clear calculator and mode registers; select two decimal places.	[ON/C] [STO] [2nd] [CMR] [FIX] 2		**0.00**
2. Select financial mode ("FIN" shows in the display).	[2nd] [Mode]	FIN	**0.00**
3. Enter number of deposits.	30 [N]	FIN	**30.00**
4. Add total desired future value and amount of deposit; store result.	8300 [+] 75 [=] [STO]	FIN	**8375.00**
5. Calculate and enter present value (total desired future value − beginning balance ÷ step 4 value × 100).	8300 [−] 5000 [÷] [RCL] [×] 100 [=] [PV]	FIN	**39.40**
6. Calculate and store (payment amount ÷ step 4 value × 100).	75 [÷] [RCL] [×] 100 [=] [STO]	FIN	**0.90**
7. Enter first estimate for %i (step 6 value or your own estimate).	[%i]	FIN	**0.90**

Determining the Interest Rate on an Account with a Beginning Balance and a Series of Regular Payments

Procedure	Press		Display
8. Calculate second estimate for %i.	[2nd] [PMT] [−] [RCL] [=] [%i]	FIN	**0.61**
9. Calculate third estimate.	[2nd] [PMT] [−] [RCL] [=] [%i]	FIN	**0.55**
10. Calculate fourth estimate.	[2nd] [PMT] [−] [RCL] [=] [%i]	FIN	**0.53**
11. Calculate fifth estimate.*	[2nd] [PMT] [−] [RCL] [=] [%i]	FIN	**0.53**
12. Select floating decimal point to show all significant digits; store result.	[FIX] 8 [STO]	FIN	**0.5289596**
13. Multiply by number of periods per year to calculate annual interest rate.	[×] 12 [=]	FIN	**6.3475153**
14. Select two decimal places.	[FIX] 2	FIN	**6.35**

*To find the interest rate with this procedure, repeat the key sequence for estimating the interest rate (steps 8 through 11) until the displayed answer equals the previous answer or until the answer reaches your desired level of accuracy. Notice that, in this case, the fifth estimate equals the fourth estimate so the iteration is complete in step 11. You might want to display more decimal places to increase the level of accuracy.

(continued on next page)

B. Finding the interest rate when the number of compounding periods does not equal the number of payment periods.

NOTE: This sequence assumes that steps 1 through 12 in part A have been performed.

	Procedure	Press		Display
13.	Select two decimal places.	[FIX] 2	FIN	**0.53**
14.	**Convert interest rate per payment period to rate per compounding period.**			
a.	Enter number of payments per year.	12 [N]	FIN	**12.00**
b.	Enter 0 (zero) for payment.	0 [PMT]	FIN	**0.00**
c.	Enter 1 (one) for present value.	1 [PV]	FIN	**1.00**
d.	Compute future value.	[2nd] [FV]	FIN	**1.07**
e.	Enter number of compounding periods per year.	52 [N]	FIN	**52.00**
f.	Compute interest rate per compounding period.	[2nd] [%i]	FIN	**0.12**
15.	**Multiply by number of compounding periods per year to calculate annual interest rate.**	[×] 52 [=]	FIN	**6.33**

C. Finding the interest rate with continuous compounding.

NOTE: This sequence assumes that steps 1 through 12 in part A have been performed.

	Procedure	Press		Display
13.	Select two decimal places.	[FIX] 2	FIN	**0.53**
14.	**Convert discrete rate to continuous rate.***			
a.	Calculate continuous rate as a decimal.	1 [+] [RCL] [%] [=] [2nd] [lnx]	FIN	**0.01**
b.	Multiply by number of payments (deposits) per year to calculate annual continuous rate.	[×] 12 [=]	FIN	**0.06**
c.	Multiply by 100 to convert rate to percent.	[×] 100 [=]	FIN	**6.33**

The annual interest rate must be 6.35% with monthly compounding, 6.33% with weekly compounding, or 6.33% with continuous compounding.

*See *Appendix A* for the formula.

CHAPTER 8

Determining the Future Value of a Series of Unequal Deposits

You plan to deposit the following amounts in your savings account at the beginning of each quarter for two years.

Quarter	1	2	3	4	5	6	7	8
Deposit	100	200	300	350	400	500	700	600

How much will you have saved at the end of the second year if the annual interest rate is 7.75% compounded quarterly?

The time line for this situation is:

Deposit	$100	$200	$300	$350	$400	$500	$700	$600	
Period	0	1	2	3	4	5	6	7	8
N	8	7	6	5	4	3	2	1	0

The deposit is the amount deposited each quarter, the period is the quarter the deposit is made, and N is the number of periods the deposit is to be compounded to calculate the future value. The total amount saved is the sum of the future values of the deposits at the end of the time period (eight quarters).

Procedure	**Press**		**Display**
1. Clear calculator and mode registers; select two decimal places.	[ON/C] [STO] [2nd] [CMR] [FIX] 2		**0.00**
2. Select financial mode ("FIN" shows in the display).	[2nd] [Mode]	FIN	**0.00**
3. Calculate and enter periodic interest rate.	7.75 [÷] 4 [=] [%i]	FIN	**1.94**
4. Compute and store future value of first deposit.	8 [N] 100 [PV] [2nd] [FV] [STO]	FIN FIN FIN	**8.00** **100.00** **116.59**
5. Compute future value of second deposit and add to memory.	7 [N] 200 [PV] [2nd] [FV] [SUM]	FIN FIN FIN	**7.00** **200.00** **228.75**

Determining the Future Value of a Series of Unequal Deposits

Procedure	Press		Display
6. Compute future value	6 [N]	FIN	**6.00**
of third deposit and	300 [PV]	FIN	**300.00**
add to memory.	[2nd] [FV] [SUM]	FIN	**336.61**
7. Compute future value	5 [N]	FIN	**5.00**
of fourth deposit and	350 [PV]	FIN	**350.00**
add to memory.	[2nd] [FV] [SUM]	FIN	**385.25**
8. Compute future value	4 [N]	FIN	**4.00**
of fifth deposit and	400 [PV]	FIN	**400.00**
add to memory.	[2nd] [FV] [SUM]	FIN	**431.91**
9. Compute future value	3 [N]	FIN	**3.00**
of sixth deposit and	500 [PV]	FIN	**500.00**
add to memory.	[2nd] [FV] [SUM]	FIN	**529.63**
10. Compute future value	2 [N]	FIN	**2.00**
of seventh deposit	700 [PV]	FIN	**700.00**
and add to memory.	[2nd] [FV] [SUM]	FIN	**727.39**
11. Compute future value	1 [N]	FIN	**1.00**
of eighth deposit and	600 [PV]	FIN	**600.00**
add to memory.	[2nd] [FV] [SUM]	FIN	**611.62**
12. Recall total amount saved.	[RCL]	FIN	**3367.76**

At the end of the second year, you will have saved $3,367.76.

NOTE: If interest is compounded continuously, or if the number of compounding periods per year does not equal the number of payment periods per year, convert the annual interest rate to an equivalent rate as shown in the example "Determining How Much Your Savings Will Be Worth with a Series of Equal Deposits" in this chapter. Then complete the problem as shown in the example above.

CHAPTER 9

FINANCIAL DECISION MAKING

Sound financial decision making is vital to the success of any business. Often, the timing of these decisions is crucial; yet the mathematical calculations required to evaluate a situation can be lengthy and tedious to perform.

Here's where the real value of your calculator comes in. With a few simple keystrokes, you can explore many financial alternatives easily. The complex calculations involved in seeing the whole picture are greatly simplified by your calculator, as we'll be exploring in this chapter.

Your calculator can't tell you when to buy or sell a particular stock or assemble a "get rich quick" scheme for you, but you'll at least be more certain that you aren't comparing "apples with oranges." Let's take a look now at how you can use your calculator to evaluate financial opportunities.

Computing Expenses as a Percent of Sales

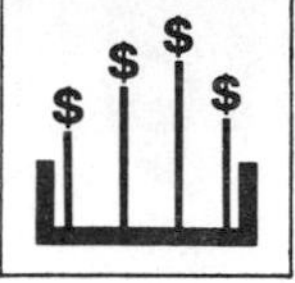

Your condensed income statement shows the following expenses:

Sales	$25,000
Cost of Sales	−15,000
Gross Margin	10,000
Selling and Administrative Expenses	−6,000
Net Income	4,000

Find each expense as a percentage of the sales.

Procedure	Press	Display
1. Clear calculator and select two decimal places.	[ON/C] [STO] [FIX] 2	**0.00**
2. Enter sales total, divide by 100, and store result.	25000 [÷] 100 [=] [STO]	**250.00**
3. Enter cost of sales and set constant to calculate percent of total sales.	15000 [÷] [K] [RCL] [=]	**60.00**
4. Enter gross margin and calculate percent of total sales.	10000 [=]	**40.00**
5. Enter selling and administrative expenses and calculate percent of total sales.	6000 [=]	**24.00**
6. Enter net income and calculate percent of total sales.	4000 [=]	**16.00**

The cost of sales is 60% of the total sales; the gross margin, 40%; the selling and administrative costs, 24%; and the net income, 16%.

CHAPTER 9

Computing Percentage Change of Actual to Budgeted Expenses

Your travel expense statement, which shows both the amount budgeted and the amount actually spent, includes these three items:

Item	*Actual*	*Budget*
Gasoline	650	500
Meals	285	300
Hotels	615	600

Find the percent change of actual expenses to budgeted expenses.

Procedure	Press	Display
1. Clear calculator and select two decimal places.	[ON/C] [FIX] 2	**0.00**
2. Enter actual gasoline expense and budgeted gasoline expense to calculate percent change.	650 [2nd] [Δ%] 500 [=]	**30.00**
3. Calculate percent change for meals.	285 [2nd] [Δ%] 300 [=]	**-5.00**
4. Calculate percent change for hotels.	615 [2nd] [Δ%] 600 [=]	**2.50**

Your gasoline expenses were 30% over budget, meals were 5% under, and hotels were 2.5% over.

Notice that percent change is calculated with respect to the second value entered (see Chapter 1 for the formula).

Determining the Equivalent Taxable Yield on Tax-Free Bonds

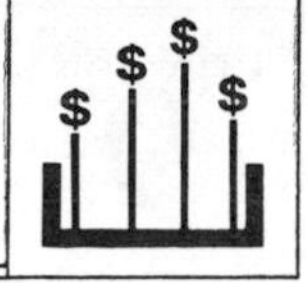

You're currently in a 45% income tax bracket and are considering buying a 6% tax-free yield municipal bond. What taxable yield would you have to earn to get the same amount after taxes?

Procedure	Press	Display
1. Clear calculator and select two decimal places.	[ON/C] [STO] [FIX] 2	**0.00**
2. Calculate nontaxable income rate (100 − income tax bracket) and store result as a decimal.	100 [−] 45 [=] [%] [STO]	**0.55**
3. Calculate equivalent taxable yield (municipal bond rate ÷ nontaxable income rate.)	6 [÷] [RCL] [=]	**10.91**

The equivalent taxable yield would be 10.91%.

Determining the Equivalent Tax-Free Yield on Taxable Bonds

You currently own a taxable bond that pays 10% dividends, and you are in a 38% income tax bracket. What dividend rate would you need to earn to get the same return?

Procedure	Press	Display
1. Clear calculator and select two decimal places.	[ON/C] [FIX] 2	**0.00**
2. Enter 100 and subtract income tax bracket percent.	100 [-] 38 [=] [%]	**0.62**
3. Multiply by taxable yield to calculate equivalent tax-free yield.	[×] 10 [=]	**6.20**

You would need to earn a 6.2% annual dividend rate on a tax-free bond.

Comparing the Cost of Whole Life and Term Insurance

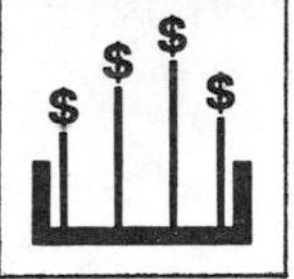

You can get $20,000 of term life insurance coverage for a $4.20 premium payment each month. Although this is a relatively low premium rate, a term policy usually builds no cash value. An insurance salesman offers you a whole life policy which will have a cash value of $5000 after 25 years, but the monthly premiums for this policy are $18. Which policy should you buy?

One way to decide is to calculate the difference in monthly premiums ($18 − $4.20 = $13.80). You know that you can earn 6% annual interest, compounded monthly, if you deposit this amount in a savings account at the first of each month. At the end of 25 years, will this monthly saving be worth more or less than the $5000 cash value of the second policy?

Procedure	Press		Display
1. Clear calculator and mode registers; select two decimal places.	[ON/C] [2nd] [CMR] [FIX] 2		**0.00**
2. Select financial mode ("FIN" shows in the display).	[2nd] [Mode]	FIN	**0.00**
3. Calculate and enter number of periodic (monthly) payments.	25 [×] 12 [=] [N]	FIN	**300.00**
4. Calculate and enter periodic (monthly) interest rate.	6 [÷] 12 [=] [%i]	FIN	**0.50**
5. Calculate and enter extra monthly premium amount.	18 [−] 4.2 [=] [PMT]	FIN	**13.80**
6. Compute value of payments at end of 25 years.	[DUE] [FV]	FIN	**9611.13**
7. Compare to cash value of whole life.	[−] 5000 [=]	FIN	**4611.13**

Buying the term insurance and depositing the premium difference in savings each month will result in an additional $4611.13 over the 25 years.

NOTE: This solution assumes that the term insurance and the interest rate remain the same and that you faithfully deposit the premium difference in a savings account each month.

CHAPTER 9

Determining Whether to Finance or Save for a Purchase

A. You are starting a new business, and you need to purchase a dictation transcriber ($285), an electric typewriter ($995), and some office furniture ($1500). But you have only $1000 set aside for office equipment. You decide to use this for a down payment and finance the rest at 15% compounded monthly for three years. What will your monthly payments be, and what would the total cost of the equipment be (including financing)? For this example, disregard tax effects.

Procedure	Press		Display
1. Clear calculator and mode registers; select two decimal places.	[ON/C] [STO] [2nd] [CMR] [FIX] 2		0.00
2. Select financial mode ("FIN" shows in the display).	[2nd] [Mode]	FIN	0.00
3. Calculate and enter number of payments.	3 [×] 12 [=] [N]	FIN	36.00
4. Calculate and enter periodic interest rate.	15 [÷] 12 [=] [%i]	FIN	1.25
5. Calculate amount of cash you need,	285 [+] 995 [+] 1500 [=]	FIN	2780.00
deduct down payment, and enter as present value.	[−] 1000 [=] [PV]	FIN	1780.00
6. Compute payment.	[2nd] [PMT]	FIN	**61.70**
7. Calculate and store total cost of items, including interest and down payment. (Leave your calculator on.)	[×] 36 [+] 1000 [=] [STO]	FIN	**3221.35**

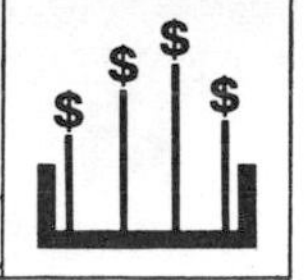

B. You decide you could really get by if you only purchased the typewriter now, paying cash, and saved for the rest. You plan to deposit each month the amount you would have made in payments, and your savings account pays 6% annual interest, compounded monthly. How long will it take you to accumulate the money you need, and how much will you save with this plan?

Procedure	Press		Display
8. Clear calculator and mode registers.	[ON/C] [2nd] [CMR]	FIN	**0.00**
9. Calculate and enter periodic interest rate on savings account.	6 [÷] 12 [=] [%i]	FIN	**0.50**
10. Enter payment amount (step 6).	61.70 [PMT]	FIN	**61.70**
11. Calculate amount you need to save and enter result as future value.	1000 [−] 995 [=] [+/−] [+] 285 [+] 1500 [=] [FV]	FIN	**1780.00**
12. Compute number of months it will take you to save amount you need.	[2nd] [N]	FIN	**27.02**
13. Multiply by payment amount and add down payment to calculate total cost of items.	[×] 61.70 [+] 1000 [=]	FIN	**2666.92**
14. Subtract plan B result from plan A result to calculate savings.	[+/−] [+] [RCL] [=]	FIN	**554.43**

You would save $554.43 by waiting and saving. Now, with this in mind, you can decide whether to wait or buy all of your equipment now.

CHAPTER
9 Capital Asset Pricing Model

Suppose an analyst wants to use the Capital Asset Pricing model to estimate the expected return on a security for the coming period. Assume that:

- the risk-free interest rate is 6%,
- the expected return on the market portfolio of securities is 9%, and
- the volatility of stock return (degree of responsiveness relative to that of the market portfolio) is 1.5.

Procedure	Press	Display
1. Clear calculator and select two decimal places.	[ON/C] [FIX] 2	**0.00**
2. Enter expected return and subtract risk-free rate.	9 [−] 6 [=]	**3.00**
3. Multiply by volatility.	[×] 1.5 [=]	**4.50**
4. Add risk-free rate.	[+] 6 [=]	**10.50**

The expected return rate is 10.5%.

See *Appendix A* for the formula.

Reference:

Weston and Brigham, *Managerial Finance,* pp. 657-660, 686.

An Economic Order Quantity Inventory Model

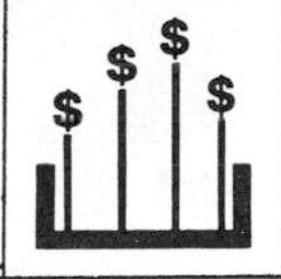

A company has annual requirements for 30,000 units, with an $18 cost per purchase order placed. The cost of carrying one unit of inventory for a year is estimated to be $0.15. What is the Economic Order Quantity (EOQ), what are the minimum annual inventory costs, and how many times per year should inventory be ordered?

The EOQ is the quantity which should be ordered to minimize inventory costs during a specified time period, assuming no stock outs. Inventory costs consist of ordering costs plus carrying costs, and this model determines the EOQ and the minimum inventory costs for the time period. You can also find the number of times to order by dividing the number of units to be used during the time period by the EOQ. (See *Appendix A* for the formula.)

Procedure	Press	Display
1. Clear calculator and select two decimal places.	[ON/C] [STO] [FIX] 2	**0.00**
2. Enter cost per purchase order and multiply by number of units needed per period.	18 [×] 30000 [=]	**540000.00**
3. Multiply by 2; store result.	[×] 2 [=] [STO]	**1080000.0**
4. Enter carrying cost per unit.	.15	**0.15**
5. Calculate economic order quantity (EOQ).	[1/x] [×] [RCL] [=] [2nd] [√x]	**2683.28**
6. Enter carrying cost; calculate minimum inventory costs per period.	.15 [×] [RCL] [=] [2nd] [√x]	**402.49**
7. Enter number of units required per period.	30000	**30000**
8. Divide by EOQ to calculate number of times to order per period.	[÷] 2683.28 [=]	**11.18**

The economic order quantity is about 2,683 units with a minimum annual inventory cost of $402.49. You would need to order 2,683 units about 11 times per year.

CHAPTER 9

A Cash Management Model

Your company wants to find the return point for its cash account and the upper allowable limit for the cash balance. You know that it costs $30 to transfer money between the cash and investment accounts and that the variance of the daily changes in the cash balance is $200,000. The annual interest rate on your investment account is 9% compounded daily.

The cash management model developed by Miller and Orr (see the reference at the end of this problem and the formula in Appendix A) minimizes the total of the expected cost of transfers between the investment and the cash accounts of a company, along with the opportunity cost of holding cash. It computes a return point (Z) to which the cash balance is returned if cash is either transferred into the investment account or obtained from the investment account. When the cash balance hits zero, cash in the amount of Z is transferred from the investment account. The lower allowable limit is assumed to be zero in this model. A statement at the end of the following example shows you how to adjust your calculations for other lower limits.

Procedure	Press	Display
1. Clear calculator and select floating decimal point.	[ON/C] [STO] [FIX] 8	**0**
2. Enter annual interest rate and divide by number of compounding periods.	9 [%] [÷] 365 [=]	**0.0002466**

A Cash Management Model

Procedure	Press	Display
3. Multiply displayed value by 4 and store result.	[×] 4 [=] [STO]	0.0009863
4. Multiply cost per transfer by variance of daily change in cash balance.	30 [×] 200000 [=]	6000000
5. Multiply displayed value by 3.	[×] 3 [=]	18000000
6. Divide by amount stored in memory.	[÷] [RCL] [=]	1.825 10
7. Calculate cube root to find return point.	[2nd] [y^x] 3 [1/x] [=]	2632.8187
8. Multiply by 3 to calculate upper allowable limit for cash balance.	[×] 3 [=]	7898.4561

If a positive minimum cash level is required in the account — for example, if your bank requires a minimum of $5000 in the account — that amount should be added to both of the above results. The return point would become $7632.82 and the upper limit $12,898.46.

References:

Miller and Orr, "A Model of the Demand for Money by Firms," pp. 413-435

Weston and Brigham, *Managerial Finance*, pp. 215-218.

CHAPTER 9

Cost of Capital

One way to minimize the cost of capital is to group all capital into *debt* and *equity* classes and determine the average cost of debt capital, the proportion of equity remaining in the capital structure, and the average cost of equity capital for various proportions of debt in the capital structure. These factors can then be used to compute the average cost of capital for each mix of capital structure. The formula used is:

$$W_c = P_d C_d + P_e C_e$$

where: W_c = average cost of capital
P_d = proportion of debt in capital structure
C_d = average cost of debt capital
P_e = proportion of equity in capital structure
C_e = average cost of equity capital

Your company has projected data regarding the cost of capital for six conditions. Find the average cost of capital for each situation.

Condition	*Debt*		*Equity*		*Average Cost of Capital (to be computed)*
	P_d	C_d	P_e	C_e	
A	.10	3.7	.90	11	10.27
B	.20	4.0	.80	11.5	10.00
C	.30	4.5	.70	13	10.45
D	.40	5.0	.60	15	11.00
E	.50	5.5	.50	17	11.25
F	.60	7.5	.40	20	12.50

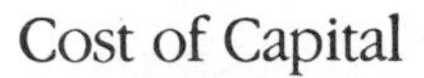

Cost of Capital

Procedure	Press	Display
1. Clear calculator and select two decimal places.	[ON/C] [STO] [FIX] 2	**0.00**
2. Enter proportion of debt in capital structure (P_d).	.10	**0.10**
3. Multiply by average cost of debt capital (C_d) and store result.	[×] 3.7 [=] [STO]	**0.37**
4. Enter proportion of equity in capital structure (P_e).	.90	**0.90**
5. Multiply by average cost of equity capital (C_e).	[×] 11 [=]	**9.90**
6. Calculate average cost of capital (W_c).	[+] [RCL] [=]	**10.27**

7. Repeat steps 2 through 6 for each condition (B through F).

Repeating this procedure for each set of data given in the example will allow computation of the average cost of capital for each situation. Capital costs are lowest where debt makes up 20% of the capital structure.

Reference:

Weston and Brigham, *Managerial Finance,* pp. 710-712.

CHAPTER 9

Determining Replacement Cost of a Product with Considerations for Inflation

Assume that on June 1, 1980, you paid $100 for a product which you held for resale. On January 1, 1981, you sell the product for $125. With an average monthly increase of 1.5% in the wholesale price of this product, how much will you pay to replace the product? If your tax rate is 40%, how much cash will you have after replacing the product?

Procedure	Press		Display
1. Clear calculator and mode registers; select two decimal places.	[ON/C] [STO] [2nd] [CMR] [FIX] 2		**0.00**
2. Select financial mode ("FIN" shows in the display).	[2nd] [Mode]	FIN	**0.00**
3. Enter number of months product was held.	7 [N]	FIN	**7.00**
4. Enter monthly inflation rate.	1.5 [%i]	FIN	**1.50**
5. Enter original cost of product.	100 [PV]	FIN	**100.00**

Determining Replacement Cost of a Product with Considerations for Inflation

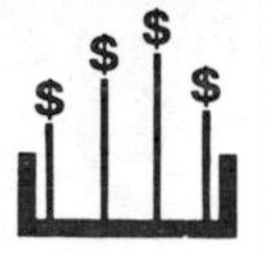

Procedure	Press		Display
6. Compute and store replacement cost.	[2nd] [FV] [STO]	FIN	**110.98**
7. Enter selling price and subtract original cost to calculate amount of taxable income.	125 [−] 100 [=]	FIN	**25.00**
8. Multiply by tax rate to calculate income tax and add to replacement cost stored in memory (step 6).	[×] 40 [%] [=] [SUM]	FIN	**10.00**
9. Calculate cash available after replacing product and paying taxes.	125 [−] [RCL] [=]	FIN	**4.02**
10. Calculate cash available *without* inflation (multiply difference in selling price and original cost by one minus tax rate).	125 [−] 100 [×] 60 [%] [=]	FIN	**15.00**

After replacing the product, you have $4.02 available cash, compared to $15 without inflation.

Determining Selling Price to Achieve a Specified Gross Margin with Inflation

In the previous example, the product which cost $100 sold for $125, resulting in a gross margin of 20% based on historical cost. We determined that the replacement cost with inflation would be $110.98. Find the sales price necessary to maintain a 20% gross margin when the cost of goods sold is based on the replacement cost.

Procedure	Press	Display
1. Clear calculator and mode registers; select two decimal places.	[ON/C] [2nd] [CMR] [FIX] 2	**0.00**
2. Select profit margin mode ("FIN" or "STAT" does *not* show in the display).	[2nd] [Mode]	**0.00**
3. Enter original cost and selling price, and compute gross profit margin.	100 [CST] 125 [SEL] [2nd] [MAR]	**100.00** **125.00** **20.00**
4. Enter replacement cost.	110.98 [CST]	**110.98**
5. Compute sales price using replacement cost.	[2nd] [SEL]	**138.73**

For a gross margin of 20% and with a replacement cost of $110.98, you need to sell the product for $138.73.

Determining the After-Tax Cash Flow with Inflation

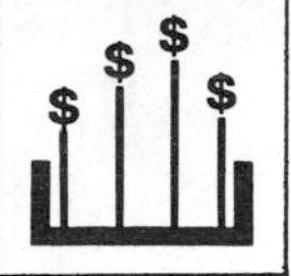

This example uses the results obtained from the two previous problems. You buy a product for $100 and sell it for $138.73. Your tax rate is 40%, and the replacement cost of the product is $110.98. How much is your after-tax cash flow?

Procedure	Press	Display
1. Clear calculator and select two decimal places.	[ON/C] [STO] [FIX] 2	**0.00**
2. Store sales price.	138.73 [STO]	**138.73**
3. Subtract purchase price.	[−] 100 [=]	**38.73**
4. Multiply by tax rate to determine income tax.	[×] 40 [%] [=]	**15.49**
5. Subtract displayed value from sales price stored in memory (step 2).	[+/−] [SUM]	**-15.49**
6. Calculate cash flow after replacing product (sales price − replacement cost).	[RCL] [−] 110.98 [=]	**12.26**

The after-tax cash flow with inflation is $12.26 for an item with a selling price which has a 20% gross margin based on replacement cost. However, this cash flow is still less than the $15 cash flow without inflation which also has a 20% gross margin so the selling price should be more than $138.73. To find out the selling price necessary to have a $15 after-tax cash flow, work the next example.

Determining Sales Price to Achieve a Specified After-Tax Cash Flow (with Inflation)

From the three previous examples, we now have a product which was originally purchased for $100 and which has a replacement cost of $110.98. The tax rate is 40%. Find the sales price necessary to have a $15 cash flow after paying taxes and replacing the product (the amount of cash available without inflation).

Procedure	Press	Display
1. Clear calculator and select two decimal places.	[ON/C] [STO] [FIX] 2	**0.00**
2. Enter required after-tax cash flow.	15	**15**
3. Add replacement cost and store result.	[+] 110.98 [=] [STO]	**125.98**
4. Enter original cost and multiply by tax rate; subtract from memory.	100 [×] 40 [%] [=] [+/−] [SUM]	**-40.00**
5. Subtract tax rate from 100 and convert to decimal to calculate nontaxable rate.	100 [−] 40 [=] [%]	**0.60**
6. Divide value in memory (steps 3 and 4) by result of step 5 to calculate sales price.	[EXC] [÷] [RCL] [=]	**143.30**

You will need to sell the product for $143.30 if you want an after tax cash flow of $15. (The GPM is 30.22% based on historical costs and 22.55% based on replacement costs.)

Average Return Rate on a Non-Dividend-Paying Stock

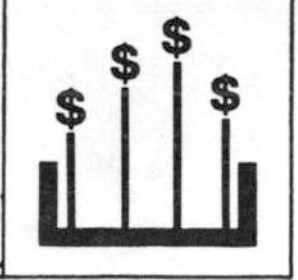

Last year you bought several shares of stock in a corporation at $98 per share. This year the stock is selling at $122 per share. The stock has paid no dividends. What is the percentage increase in value that you could collect if you sold the stock? Ignore any sales fees to sell the stock.

Procedure	Press		Display
1. Clear calculator and mode registers; select two decimal places.	[ON/C] [2nd] [CMR] [FIX] 2		**0.00**
2. Select financial mode ("FIN" shows in the display).	[2nd] [Mode]	FIN	**0.00**
3. Enter number of periods.	1 [N]	FIN	**1.00**
4. Enter original value of stock.	98 [PV]	FIN	**98.00**
5. Enter new value.	122 [FV]	FIN	**122.00**
6. Calculate average annual return.	[2nd] [%i]	FIN	**24.49**

The yield is about 24.5%.

CHAPTER 9

Determining the Theoretical Value of a Stock Paying Constant Dividends

You have an opportunity to buy a stock which pays a $0.65 dividend at the end of each quarter. The stock would probably sell for $180 at the end of four years. If you want an annual return rate of 18% compounded quarterly, how much would you be willing to pay for the stock, disregarding taxes?

The theoretical stock price is the sum of the present value of the selling price (steps 3 through 6) and the present value of the quarterly dividends (steps 7 and 8).

Procedure	Press		Display
1. Clear calculator and mode registers; select two decimal places.	[ON/C] [STO] [2nd] [CMR] [FIX] 2		**0.00**
2. Select financial mode ("FIN" shows in the display).	[2nd] [Mode]	FIN	**0.00**
3. Calculate and enter number of dividend payments.	4 [×] 4 [=] [N]	FIN	**16.00**
4. Calculate and enter return rate per dividend period.	18 [÷] 4 [=] [%i]	FIN	**4.50**
5. Enter future value of stock.	180 [FV]	FIN	**180.00**
6. Compute and store present value of stock.	[2nd] [PV] [STO]	FIN	**89.00**
7. Enter dividend amount.	.65 [PMT]	FIN	**0.65**
8. Compute present value of dividends and add to memory.	[2nd] [PV] [SUM]	FIN	**7.30**
9. Recall theoretical stock price.	[RCL]	FIN	**96.31**

You could pay up to $96.31 for the stock in order to earn your desired rate of return.

Average Return Rate on a Non-Dividend-Paying Stock, Including Sale Commissions and Taxes

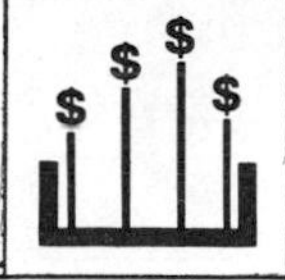

Three years ago you purchased some stock for $35 per share plus a 1 1/2% commission per share. You now have an opportunity to sell the stock for $48 a share less a 1.75% commission. The tax on the gain would be 17%. If you decide to sell, what is your after-tax return rate?

Procedure	Press		Display
1. Clear calculator and mode registers; select two decimal places.	[ON/C] [STO] [2nd] [CMR] [FIX] 2		**0.00**
2. Select financial mode ("FIN" shows in the display).	[2nd] [Mode]	FIN	**0.00**
3. Enter number of years.	3 [N]	FIN	**3.00**
4. Enter sales price of stock, subtract commission, and store result.	48 [−] 1.75 [%] [=] [STO]	FIN	**47.16**
5. Enter purchase price of stock plus commission.	35 [+] 1.5 [%] [=] [PV]	FIN	**35.53**
6. Subtract net purchase price (step 5) from net sales price (step 4) to calculate taxable gain on sale.	[+/−] [+] [RCL] [=]	FIN	**11.64**
7. Multiply by tax rate to calculate tax liability.	[×] 17 [%] [=]	FIN	**1.98**
8. Subtract tax (step 7) from net sales price (step 4) to calculate after-tax cash flow from sale; enter result.	[+/−] [+] [RCL] [=] [FV]	FIN	**45.18**
9. Compute annual rate of return.	[2nd] [%i]	FIN	**8.35**

Your after-tax annual rate of return would be 8.35%.

Average Return Rate on Stock Paying Constant Dividends

The stock which you purchased two years ago for $53 per share plus a 1.75% commission per share has paid dividends of $0.35 at the end of each quarter. The stock's current sales price is $65 less a 1.5% commission. Ignoring taxes, find the average annual return rate, compounded quarterly.

Since the equation cannot directly solve for the return rate, the result must be found by a repetitive, trial-and-error process known as an iteration. See steps 5 through 12.

Procedure	Press		Display
1. Clear calculator and mode registers; select two decimal places.	[ON/C] [STO] [2nd] [CMR] [FIX] 2		**0.00**
2. Select financial mode ("FIN" shows in the display).	[2nd] [Mode]	FIN	**0.00**
3. Calculate and enter number of dividend payments.	2 [×] 4 [=] [N]	FIN	**8.00**
4. Enter purchase price of stock, add commission, and store result.	53 [+] 1.75 [%] [=] [STO]	FIN	**53.93**
5. Enter sales price of stock and subtract commission.	65 [−] 1.5 [%] [=]	FIN	**64.03**
6. Calculate and enter future value to find interest rate (step 5 value − step 4 value ÷ step 4 value × 100).	[−] [RCL] [÷] [RCL] [×] 100 [=] [FV]	FIN	**18.72**

Average Return Rate on Stock Paying Constant Dividends

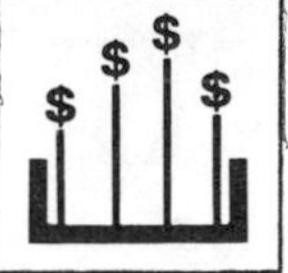

Procedure	Press		Display
7. Calculate and store (dividend amount ÷ step 4 value × 100).	.35 [÷] [RCL] [×] 100 [=] [STO]	FIN	**0.65**
8. Enter first estimate for %i (step 7 value or your own estimate).	[%i]	FIN	**0.65**
9. Calculate second estimate of %i.	[2nd] [PMT] [+] [RCL] [=] [%i]	FIN	**2.94**
10. Calculate third estimate.	[2nd] [PMT] [+] [RCL] [=] [%i]	FIN	**2.76**
11. Calculate fourth estimate.	[2nd] [PMT] [+] [RCL] [=] [%i]	FIN	**2.77**
12. Calculate fifth estimate.*	[2nd] [PMT] [+] [RCL] [=] [%i]	FIN	**2.77**
13. Multiply by number of periods per year to calculate average annual return rate.	[×] 4 [=]	FIN	**11.09**

The average annual return rate on this stock would be 11.09%.

*To find the return rate with this procedure, repeat the key sequence for estimating the interest rate (steps 9 through 12) until the displayed answer equals the previous answer or until the answer reaches your desired level of accuracy. Notice that, in this case, the fifth estimate equals the fourth estimate so the iteration is complete in step 12. You might want to display more decimal places to increase the level of accuracy.

CHAPTER 9

After-Tax Return Rate on a Stock Paying Constant Dividends

You have received a $0.50 dividend at the end of each quarter on the stock you bought five years ago for $20 per share plus a 1% commission per share. The stock is currently selling for $28 less a 1.25% commission. The tax rate on the dividends is 40%, and the tax rate on the gain is 16%. If you sell the stock, what is your after-tax annual return rate?

Since the equation cannot directly solve for the return rate, the solution must be found by a repetitive, trial-and-error process known as an iteration. See steps 12 through 18.

Procedure	Press		Display
1. Clear calculator and mode registers; select floating decimal point.	[ON/C] [STO] [2nd] [CMR] [FIX] 8		**0**
2. Select financial mode ("FIN" shows in the display).	[2nd] [Mode]	FIN	**0**
3. Calculate and enter number of dividend payments.	5 [×] 4 [=] [N]	FIN	**20**
4. Enter purchase price of stock, add commission, and store result.	20 [+] 1 [%] [=] [STO]	FIN	**20.2**
5. Enter sales price of stock less commission.	28 [−] 1.25 [%] [=]	FIN	**27.65**
6. Calculate taxable gain (step 5 − step 4).	[−] [EXC] [=]	FIN	**7.45**
7. Multiply by tax rate to find tax liability on gain.	[×] 16 [%] [=]	FIN	**1.192**
8. Subtract tax (step 7) from net sales price (step 5) to calculate after-tax cash flow from sale.	[+/−] [+] [RCL] [=]	FIN	**26.458**
9. Enter dividend amount and subtract tax on dividend to calculate after-tax dividend.	.50 [−] 40 [%] [=]	FIN	**0.3**

After-Tax Return Rate on a Stock Paying Constant Dividends

Procedure	Press		Display
10. Enter purchase price, add commission, and store result.	20 [+] 1 [%] [=] [STO]	FIN	**20.2**
11. Select number of decimal places for desired accuracy level.	[FIX] 2	FIN	**20.20**
12. Calculate future value (after-tax cash flow from step 8 − step 10 value ÷ step 10 value × 100).	26.458 [−] [RCL] [÷] [RCL] [×] 100 [=] [FV]	FIN	**30.98**
13. Calculate and store (after-tax dividend ÷ step 10 value × 100).	.3 [÷] [RCL] [×] 100 [=] [STO]	FIN	**1.49**
14. Enter first estimate for %i (step 13 value or your own estimate).	[%i]	FIN	**1.49**
15. Calculate second estimate for %i.	[2nd] [PMT] [+] [RCL] [=] [%i]	FIN	**2.83**
16. Calculate third estimate.	[2nd] [PMT] [+] [RCL] [=] [%i]	FIN	**2.66**
17. Calculate fourth estimate.	[2nd] [PMT] [+] [RCL] [=] [%i]	FIN	**2.68**
18. Calculate fifth estimate.*	[2nd] [PMT] [+] [RCL] [=] [%i]	FIN	**2.68**
19. Multiply by number of dividend periods per year to calculate annual return rate.	[×] 4 [=]	FIN	**10.71**

Your after-tax annual return rate would be 10.71% compounded quarterly.

*To find the return rate with this procedure, repeat the key sequence for estimating the interest rate (steps 15 through 18) until the displayed answer equals the previous answer or until the answer reaches your desired level of accuracy. You might want to display more decimal places to increase the level of accuracy.

CHAPTER

9 Finding the Value of a Growth Stock

Sometimes a particular stock will be expected to experience "supernormal growth." That is, for a limited, predictable period, it will grow at a much faster rate than the economy as a whole and then drop back to a lower growth rate.

You are investigating a stock that currently pays a dividend of $2.20 annually, but is expected to grow at a supernormal rate of 25% per year for the next eight years. Then it will drop back to a normal growth rate of 5% per year. What is the value of the stock? (Your company requires an annual rate of return of 11% per year on all investments.)

The total stock price is the sum of the stock price at the end of the supernormal growth period discounted back to the present (steps 3 through 11) and the present value of the dividends received during the supernormal growth period (steps 12 and 13).*

Procedure	Press		Display
1. Clear calculator and mode registers; select two decimal places.	[ON/C] [STO] [2nd] [CMR] [FIX] 2		0.00
2. Select financial mode ("FIN" shows in the display).	[2nd] [Mode]	FIN	0.00
3. Enter number of supernormal growth periods.	8 [N]	FIN	8.00
4. Enter 1, add rate of return per investment period, and store result.	1 [+] 11 [%] [=] [STO]	FIN	1.11
5. Enter supernormal growth rate and add 1 (one).	25 [%] [+] 1 [=]	FIN	1.25
6. Divide value in memory (step 4) by result of step 5.	[EXC] [÷] [RCL] [=]	FIN	0.89

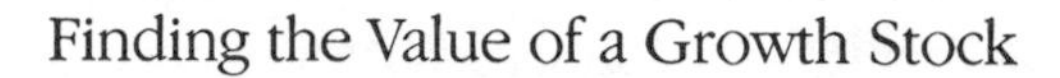
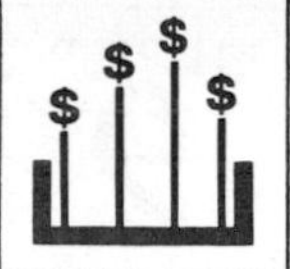

Finding the Value of a Growth Stock

	Procedure	Press		Display
7.	Subtract 1 (one) and multiply by 100 to find equivalent interest rate for calculations; enter rate.	[−] 1 [×] 100 [=] [%i]	FIN	−11.20
8.	Enter rate of return, subtract normal growth rate per dividend period, and store result.	11 [−] 5 [=] [%] [STO]	FIN	0.06
9.	Add dividend payment and normal growth rate.	2.20 [+] 5 [%] [=]	FIN	2.31
10.	Divide by step 8 value to calculate and enter future value of dividends.	[÷] [RCL] [=] [FV]	FIN	38.50
11.	Compute and store present value of stock.	[2nd] [PV] [STO]	FIN	99.58
12.	Enter dividend payment.	2.20 [PMT]	FIN	2.20
13.	Compute present value of supernormal growth dividends and add to memory.	[2nd] [PV] [SUM]	FIN	31.16
14.	**Recall theoretical stock value.**	[RCL]	FIN	130.74

The theoretical value of the stock is $130.74.

*See *Appendix A* for the formulas.

Reference:

Weston and Brigham, *Managerial Finance,* pp. 647-651.

CHAPTER 9

Finding the Effect of a Constant Percent Increase on a Series of Cash Flows

The current maintenance cost on one of your machines is $1000 per year, paid at the end of the year, and you expect an annual increase in maintenance cost of 12%. You want to deposit a single sum today to establish a repair fund to cover the expenses for the next five years. If the annual interest earned on the fund will be 10%, how much do you need to deposit, both with and without the annual increase?

Procedure	Press		Display
1. Clear calculator and mode registers; select two decimal places.	ON/C STO 2nd CMR FIX 2		0.00
2. Select financial mode ("FIN" shows in the display).	2nd Mode	FIN	0.00
3. Enter number of periods.	5 N	FIN	5.00
4. Enter current maintenance cost.	1000 PMT	FIN	1000.00
5. Enter interest rate plus 1; store result.	10 % + 1 = STO	FIN	1.10
6. Enter growth rate per payment period and add 1.	12 % + 1 =	FIN	1.12

Finding the Effect of a Constant Percent Increase on a Series of Cash Flows

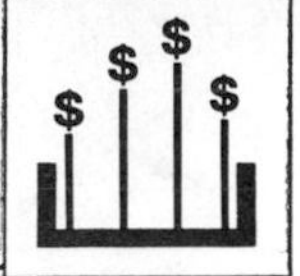

Procedure	Press		Display
7. Divide value in memory (step 5) by result of step 6.	[EXC] [÷] [RCL] [=]	FIN	**0.98**
8. Subtract 1 (one) and multiply by 100 to find equivalent interest rate for calculations.	[−] 1 [×] 100 [=] [%i]	FIN	**-1.79**
9. Compute and store present value of payments with growth rate.	[2nd] [PV] [STO]	FIN	**5279.43**
10. Enter earnings rate without growth rate.	10 [%i]	FIN	**10.00**
11. Compute present value without growth rate.	[2nd] [PV]	FIN	**3790.79**
12. Calculate difference of steps 9 and 11.	[+/−] [+] [RCL] [=]	FIN	**1488.64**

Due to the increase in maintenance costs, you will need to deposit $1,488.64 more than you would if no increase were expected.

Reference:

Greynolds, Aronofsky, and Frame, *Financial Analysis Using Calculators: Time Value of Money*, pp. 390-394.

CHAPTER 9 Solving for Payment Amount of a Sinking Fund (Payments Made at End of Periods)

Your company wants to have $50,000 in a sinking fund at the end of five years. Semiannual payments will be made at the end of each period into an account with an annual interest rate of 7%. Find the semiannual deposit necessary if interest is compounded (a) semiannually, (b) monthly, or (c) continuously.

A. Finding the payment amount when the number of compounding periods equals the number of payment periods.

Procedure	Press		Display
1. Clear calculator and mode registers; select two decimal places.	ON/C 2nd CMR FIX 2		0.00
2. Select financial mode ("FIN" shows in the display).	2nd Mode	FIN	0.00
3. Calculate and enter number of payments.	5 × 2 = N	FIN	10.00
4. Calculate and enter periodic interest rate.	7 ÷ 2 = %i	FIN	3.50
5. Enter future value.	50000 FV	FIN	50000.00
6. Compute payment amount.	2nd PMT	FIN	4262.07

B. Finding the payment amount when the number of compounding periods does not equal the number of payment periods.

Procedure	Press		Display
1. Clear calculator and mode registers; select two decimal places.	ON/C 2nd CMR FIX 2		0.00
2. Select financial mode ("FIN" shows in the display).	2nd Mode	FIN	0.00

Solving for Payment Amount of a Sinking Fund (Payments Made at End of Periods)

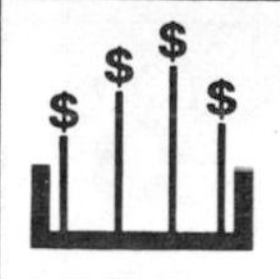

Procedure	Press		Display
3. Convert interest rate per compounding period to rate per payment period.			
a. Enter number of compounding periods per year.	12 [N]	FIN	**12.00**
b. Calculate and enter interest rate per compounding period.	7 [÷] 12 [=] [%i]	FIN	**0.58**
c. Enter 1 (one) for present value.	1 [PV]	FIN	**1.00**
d. Compute future value.	[2nd] [FV]	FIN	**1.07**
e. Enter number of payment periods per year.	2 [N]	FIN	**2.00**
f. Compute interest rate per payment period.	[2nd] [%i]	FIN	**3.55**
4. Calculate and enter number of deposits.	5 [×] 2 [=] [N]	FIN	**10.00**
5. Enter future value.	50000 [FV]	FIN	**50000.00**
6. Compute payment amount.	[2nd] [PMT]	FIN	**4251.95**

(continued on next page)

C. Finding the payment amount with continuous compounding.

Procedure	Press		Display
1. Clear calculator and mode registers; select two decimal places.	[ON/C] [2nd] [CMR] [FIX] 2		**0.00**
2. Select financial mode ("FIN" shows in the display).	[2nd] [Mode]	FIN	**0.00**
3. Calculate and enter number of periods.	5 [×] 2 [=] [N]	FIN	**10.00**
4. Convert continuous interest rate to equivalent discrete rate.*			
a. Divide annual rate by number of payments per year.	7 [%] [÷] 2 [=]	FIN	**0.04**
b. Calculate equivalent discrete rate.	[2nd] [eˣ] [−] 1 [=]	FIN	**0.04**
c. Convert to percent and enter equivalent discrete rate.	[×] 100 [=] [%i]	FIN	**3.56**
5. Enter future value.	50000 [FV]	FIN	**50000.00**
6. Compute payment amount.	[2nd] [PMT]	FIN	**4249.88**

The semiannual payments should be $4262.07 with semiannual compounding, $4251.95 with monthly compounding, or $4249.88 with continuous compounding.

*See *Appendix A* for the formula.

Solving for the Future Value of a Sinking Fund

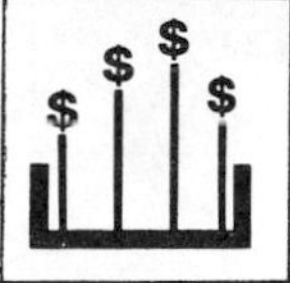

Your company is planning to deposit $5000 into a sinking fund at the end of each quarter. How much will be in the account after six years if the annual interest rate is 8% compounded quarterly?

Procedure	Press		Display
1. Clear calculator and mode registers; select two decimal places.	[ON/C] [2nd] [CMR] [FIX] 2		**0.00**
2. Select financial mode ("FIN" shows in the display).	[2nd] [Mode]	FIN	**0.00**
3. Calculate and enter number of payments.	6 [×] 4 [=] [N]	FIN	**24.00**
4. Calculate and enter periodic interest rate.	8 [÷] 4 [=] [%i]	FIN	**2.00**
5. Enter payment amount.	5000 [PMT]	FIN	**5000.00**
6. Compute future value.	[2nd] [FV]	FIN	**152109.31**

After six years, you will have $152,109.31 in the account.

In comparison, you would have $152,454.36 with weekly compounding and $152,483.55 with continuous compounding. To compute these values, follow the procedure shown in the example "Solving for Payment Amount of a Sinking Fund (Payments Made at End of Periods)" in this chapter. Convert the interest rate, enter the other two known values ([N] and [PMT]), and solve for the unknown value ([2nd] [FV]).

CHAPTER 9

Solving for the Interest Rate of a Sinking Fund

Your business can deposit $475 in a sinking fund at the end of each month. You want to save $38,000 in five years. What is the required annual interest rate with (a) monthly compounding, (b) weekly compounding, or (c) continuous compounding?

A. Finding the interest rate when the number of compounding periods equals the number of payment periods.

Procedure	Press		Display
1. Clear calculator and mode registers; select two decimal places.	ON/C 2nd CMR FIX 2		**0.00**
2. Select financial mode ("FIN" shows in the display).	2nd Mode	FIN	**0.00**
3. Calculate and enter number of payments.	5 × 12 = N	FIN	**60.00**
4. Enter amount of payment.	475 PMT	FIN	**475.00**
5. Enter future value.	38000 FV	FIN	**38000.00**
6. Compute interest rate per payment period.	2nd %i	FIN	**0.94**
7. Multiply by number of payments per year to calculate annual interest rate.	× 12 =	FIN	**11.23**

B. Finding the interest rate when the number of compounding periods does not equal the number of payment periods.

Procedure	Press		Display
1. Clear calculator and mode registers; select two decimal places.	ON/C 2nd CMR FIX 2		**0.00**
2. Select financial mode ("FIN" shows in the display).	2nd Mode	FIN	**0.00**
3. Calculate and enter number of payments.	5 × 12 = N	FIN	**60.00**

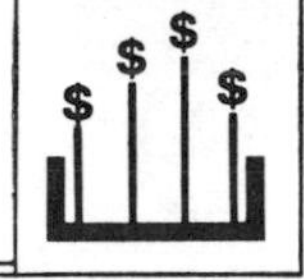

Procedure	Press		Display
4. Enter amount of payment.	475 [PMT]	FIN	**475.00**
5. Enter future value.	38000 [FV]	FIN	**38000.00**
6. Compute interest rate per payment period.	[2nd] [%i]	FIN	**0.94**
7. Convert interest rate per payment period to rate per compounding period.			
a. Enter 0 (zero) for payment.	0 [PMT]	FIN	**0.00**
b. Enter number of payments per year.	12 [N]	FIN	**12.00**
c. Enter 1 (one) for present value.	1 [PV]	FIN	**1.00**
d. Compute future value.	[2nd] [FV]	FIN	**1.12**
e. Enter number of compounding periods per year.	52 [N]	FIN	**52.00**
f. Compute interest rate per compounding period.	[2nd] [%i]	FIN	**0.22**
8. Multiply by number of compounding periods per year to calculate annual interest rate.	[×] 52 [=]	FIN	**11.19**

C. Finding the interest rate with continuous compounding.

Procedure	Press		Display
1. Clear calculator and mode registers; select two decimal places.	[ON/C] [2nd] [CMR] [FIX] 2		**0.00**
2. Select financial mode ("FIN" shows in the display).	[2nd] [Mode]	FIN	**0.00**

(continued on next page)

Procedure	Press		Display
3. Calculate and enter number of payments.	5 [X] 12 [=] [N]	FIN	**60.00**
4. Enter amount of payment.	475 [PMT]	FIN	**475.00**
5. Enter future value.	38000 [FV]	FIN	**38000.00**
6. Compute discrete interest rate per payment period.	[2nd] [%i]	FIN	**0.94**
7. Convert discrete interest rate to equivalent continuous rate.*			
a. Convert percent to decimal.	[%]	FIN	**0.01**
b. Calculate continuous rate per payment period as a decimal.	[+] 1 [=] [2nd] [lnx]	FIN	**0.01**
c. Multiply by number of payments per year to calculate annual interest rate.	[X] 12 [=]	FIN	**0.11**
d. Multiply by 100 to find rate as a percent.	[X] 100 [=]	FIN	**11.17**

Your business would need an annual interest rate of 11.23% with monthly compounding, 11.19% with daily compounding, or 11.17% with continuous compounding.

*See *Appendix A* for the formula.

Solving for the Required Number of Payments for a Sinking Fund

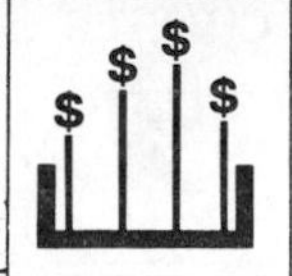

Your company is depositing $5000 at the end of each quarter and wants to accumulate $150,000. How many deposits will be necessary with an annual interest rate of 8.5% compounded quarterly?

Procedure	Press		Display
1. Clear calculator and mode registers; select two decimal places.	[ON/C] [2nd] [CMR] [FIX] 2		0.00
2. Select financial mode ("FIN" shows in the display).	[2nd] [Mode]	FIN	0.00
3. Calculate and enter periodic interest rate.	8.5 [÷] 4 [=] [%i]	FIN	2.13
4. Enter amount of payment.	5000 [PMT]	FIN	5000.00
5. Enter future value.	150000 [FV]	FIN	150000.00
6. Compute number of payments.	[2nd] [N]	FIN	**23.45**

Since your company probably would not make a partial payment, 24 payments would be required if interest is compounded quarterly.

Your company would also need to make 24 payments with monthly or continuous compounding. You can verify these facts by following the steps in "Solving for Payment Amount of a Sinking Fund (Payments Made at End of Periods)" in this chapter. Convert the interest rate, enter the other two known values ([FV] and [PMT]), and solve for the unknown value ([2nd] [N]).

CHAPTER 9

How Much Should You Pay for an Annuity?

You are considering the purchase of an annuity which will pay $500 at the end of each month for the next 20 years. How much should you pay for the annuity if the annual interest rate is 9% compounded (a) monthly, (b) quarterly, or (c) continuously?

An annuity is a series of cash flows of equal amounts. If you invest a specified amount at a given interest rate, you will receive cash payments at the end of each payment period.

A. Finding the value of an annuity when the number of compounding periods equals the number of payment periods.

Procedure	Press		Display
1. Clear calculator and mode registers; select two decimal places.	[ON/C] [2nd] [CMR] [FIX] 2		**0.00**
2. Select financial mode ("FIN" shows in the display).	[2nd] [Mode]	FIN	**240.00**
3. Calculate and enter number of payments.	20 [×] 12 [=] [N]	FIN	**240.00**
4. Calculate and enter periodic interest rate.	9 [÷] 12 [=] [%i]	FIN	**0.75**
5. Enter amount of payment.	500 [PMT]	FIN	**500.00**
6. Compute present value.	[2nd] [PV]	FIN	**55572.48**

B. Finding the value of an annuity when the number of compounding periods does not equal the number of payment periods.

Procedure	Press		Display
1. Clear calculator and mode registers; select two decimal places.	[ON/C] [2nd] [CMR] [FIX] 2		**0.00**
2. Select financial mode ("FIN" shows in the display).	[2nd] [Mode]	FIN	**0.00**

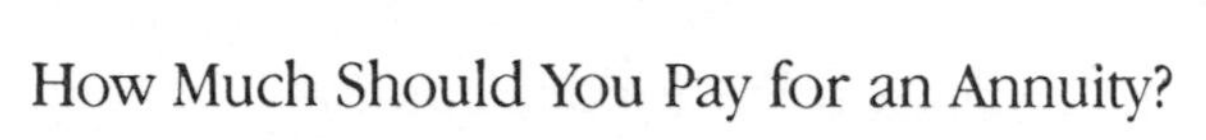

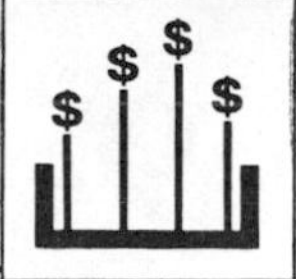

Procedure	Press		Display
3. Convert interest rate per compounding period to rate per payment period.			
a. Enter number of compounding periods per year.	4 [N]	FIN	**4.00**
b. Calculate and enter interest rate per compounding period.	9 [÷] 4 [=] [%i]	FIN	**2.25**
c. Enter 1 (one) for present value.	1 [PV]	FIN	**1.00**
d. Compute future value.	[2nd] [FV]	FIN	**1.09**
e. Enter number of payment periods per year.	12 [N]	FIN	**12.00**
f. Compute interest rate per payment period.	[2nd] [%i]	FIN	**0.74**
4. Calculate and enter number of deposits.	20 [×] 12 [=] [N]	FIN	**240.00**
5. Enter amount of payment.	500 [PMT]	FIN	**500.00**
6. Compute present value.	[2nd] [PV]	FIN	**55838.30**

(continued on next page)

C. Finding the value of an annuity with continuous compounding.

Procedure	Press		Display
1. Clear calculator and mode registers; select two decimal places.	[ON/C] [2nd] [CMR] [FIX] 2		0.00
2. Select financial mode ("FIN" shows in the display).	[2nd] [Mode]	FIN	0.00
3. Calculate and enter number of periods.	20 [×] 12 [=] [N]	FIN	240.00
4. Convert continous interest rate to equivalent discrete rate.*			
a. Divide annual rate by number of payments per year and convert to decimal.	9 [÷] 12 [=] [%]	FIN	0.01
b. Calculate equivalent discrete rate.	[2nd] [eˣ] [−] 1 [=]	FIN	0.01
c. Convert to percent and enter equivalent discrete rate.	[×] 100 [=] [%i]	FIN	0.75
5. Enter amount of payment.	500 [PMT]	FIN	500.00
6. Compute present value.	[2nd] [PV]	FIN	**55438.33**

The value of the annuity is $55,572.48 with monthly compounding, $55,838.30 with quarterly compounding, or $55,438.33 with continuous compounding.

*See *Appendix A* for the formula.

Determining the Payment Received from an Annuity

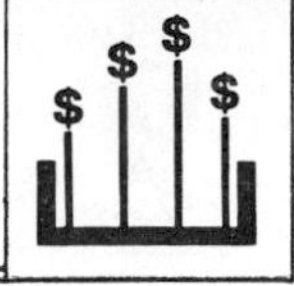

You are planning to invest $20,000 in a 15-year annuity. How much will you receive at the end of each month if the annual interest rate is 9% compounded monthly?

Procedure	Press		Display
1. Clear calculator and mode registers; select two decimal places.	[ON/C] [2nd] [CMR] [FIX] 2		0.00
2. Select financial mode ("FIN" shows in the display).	[2nd] [Mode]	FIN	0.00
3. Calculate and enter number of payments.	15 [×] 12 [=] [N]	FIN	180.00
4. Calculate and enter periodic interest rate.	9 [÷] 12 [=] [%i]	FIN	0.75
5. Enter amount of investment.	20000 [PV]	FIN	20000.00
6. Compute payment.	[2nd] [PMT]	FIN	**202.85**

At the end of each month, you will receive $202.85 with an annual interest rate of 9% compounded monthly.

If interest is compounded weekly, you will receive $203.16 at the end of each month. With continuous compounding, you would receive $203.26. To solve for either of these, convert the interest rate and enter the other two known values ([N] and [PV]) as described in "How Much Should You Pay for an Annuity?" in this chapter. Then compute the unknown value ([2nd] [PMT]).

CHAPTER 9

Determining the Interest Rate on an Annuity

You have an opportunity to buy a $50,000 annuity which will pay $570 at the end of each month for 10 years. What is the annual interest rate with (a) monthly compounding, (b) quarterly compounding, or (c) continuous compounding?

A. Finding the interest rate when the number of compounding periods equals the number of payment periods.

Procedure	Press		Display
1. Clear calculator and mode registers; select two decimal places.	[ON/C] [2nd] [CMR] [FIX] 2		**0.00**
2. Select financial mode ("FIN" shows in the display).	[2nd] [Mode]	FIN	**0.00**
3. Calculate and enter number of payments.	10 [×] 12 [=] [N]	FIN	**120.00**
4. Enter amount of payment.	570 [PMT]	FIN	**570.00**
5. Enter amount of investment.	50000 [PV]	FIN	**50000.00**
6. Compute interest rate per compounding period.	[2nd] [%i]	FIN	**0.55**
7. Multiply by number of periods per year to calculate annual interest rate.	[×] 12 [=]	FIN	**6.59**

B. Finding the interest rate when the number of compounding periods does not equal the number of payment periods.

Procedure	Press		Display
1. Clear calculator and mode registers; select two decimal places.	[ON/C] [2nd] [CMR] [FIX] 2		**0.00**
2. Select financial mode ("FIN" shows in the display).	[2nd] [Mode]	FIN	**0.00**

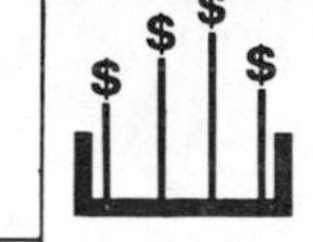

Procedure	Press		Display
3. Calculate and enter number of payments.	10 [×] 12 [=] [N]	FIN	**120.00**
4. Enter amount of payment.	570 [PMT]	FIN	**570.00**
5. Enter amount of investment.	50000 [PV]	FIN	**50000.00**
6. Compute interest rate per payment period.	[2nd] [%i]	FIN	**0.55**
7. Convert interest rate per payment period to rate per compounding period.			
a. Enter 0 (zero) for payment.	0 [PMT]	FIN	**0.00**
b. Enter number of payments per year.	12 [N]	FIN	**12.00**
c. Enter 1 (one) for present value.	1 [PV]	FIN	**1.00**
d. Compute future value.	[2nd] [FV]	FIN	**1.07**
e. Enter number of compounding periods per year.	4 [N]	FIN	**4.00**
f. Compute interest rate per compounding period.	[2nd] [%i]	FIN	**1.66**
8. Multiply by number of compounding periods per year to calculate annual interest rate.	[×] 4 [=]	FIN	**6.62**

(continued on next page)

C. Finding the interest rate with continuous compounding.

Procedure	Press		Display
1. Clear calculator and mode registers; select two decimal places.	[ON/C] [2nd] [CMR] [FIX] 2		**0.00**
2. Select financial mode ("FIN" shows in the display).	[2nd] [Mode]	FIN	**0.00**
3. Calculate and enter number of payments.	10 [×] 12 [=] [N]	FIN	**120.00**
4. Enter amount of payment.	570 [PMT]	FIN	**570.00**
5. Enter amount of investment.	50000 [PV]	FIN	**50000.00**
6. Compute discrete interest rate per payment period.	[2nd] [%i]	FIN	**0.55**
7. Convert discrete interest rate to equivalent continuous rate.*			
a. Convert percent to decimal.	[%]	FIN	**0.01**
b. Calculate continuous rate as a decimal.	[+] 1 [=] [2nd] [lnx]	FIN	**0.01**
c. Multiply by number of payments per year to calculate annual interest rate.	[×] 12 [=]	FIN	**0.07**
d. Multiply by 100 to find rate as a percent.	[×] 100 [=]	FIN	**6.57**

The annual interest rate is 6.59% with monthly compounding, 6.62% with quarterly compounding, or 6.57% with continuous compounding.

*See *Appendix A* for the formula.

Determining the Number of Annuity Payments

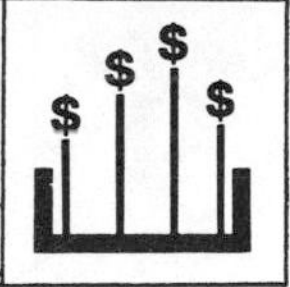

You are considering a $15,000 annuity and would like to receive $300 at the end of each month. How many payments will you receive if the annual interest rate is 12.5% compounded monthly?

Procedure	Press		Display
1. Clear calculator and mode registers; select two decimal places.	[ON/C] [2nd] [CMR] [FIX] 2		**0.00**
2. Select financial mode ("FIN" shows in the display).	[2nd] [Mode]	FIN	**0.00**
3. Calculate and enter periodic interest rate.	12.5 [÷] 12 [=] [%i]	FIN	**1.04**
4. Enter amount of payment.	300 [PMT]	FIN	**300.00**
5. Enter amount of investment.	15000 [PV]	FIN	**15000.00**
6. Compute number of payments.	[2nd] [N]	FIN	**71.00**

You will receive 71 payments with monthly compounding.

Also, you would receive 70.15 payments with semiannual compounding or 71.17 payments with continuous compounding. These results can be calculated by applying the procedure in the example "How Much Should You Pay for an Annuity?" in this chapter to this situation. Simply convert the interest rate, enter the other two known values ([PMT] and [PV]), and solve for the unknown value ([2nd] [N]).

Purchasing a Commercial Bond

A bond is a financial obligation made by a corporation or a government agency. The purchaser of a bond receives periodic interest payments, usually semiannually, and receives the face value of the bond on the redemption date.

The interest payment each period is the interest rate printed on the bond divided by the number of payments per year and multiplied by the face value of the bond. For example, each six months a 7% $1000 bond with interest paid semiannually would pay:

$$\frac{.07}{2} \times \$1000 = \$35$$

This semiannual interest payment is also called the *coupon payment*. (The word coupon refers to the fact that the semiannual payment is usually collected by presenting the company a printed coupon from a sheet that is part of the bond.) In this case, each coupon payment is $35, or 3.5%. This payment amount and the rate based on the face value of the bond remain constant. But bonds often sell at prices above or below the face value. A bond selling for an amount greater than the face (or par) value is said to be sold at a *premium* while a bond priced below par sells at a *discount.* The actual selling price can differ from the par value for many reasons. For example, a bond was originally sold when 5% was an acceptable return, but 8% is required currently in the market. Therefore, the bond would have to be sold below par (at a discount) to allow for the change in the return required in the market. This return required by the market is called *yield.*

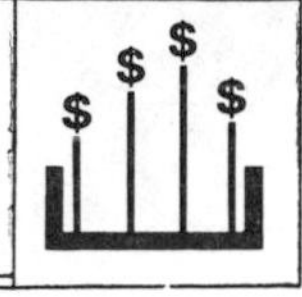

More specifically, the yield is the return desired by the buyer. Because the face value of the bond and dollar amount of the coupon payment are fixed, the selling price, or present value, of the bond is adjusted to arrive at the yield. Thus, a bond sells at a premium when its coupon rate exceeds the market yield, while a bond sells at a discount if its coupon rate is below the market yield. The yield desired by an investor is a function of many factors: the issuer's bond rating, the state of the economy, and the amount of bonds purchased, to name a few.

Your calculator will compute bond price with great accuracy. The following examples illustrate determining purchase price based on the purchase date, solving for the yield on a bond purchased on an interest date, and amortizing a bond premium or discount.

The approaches included here for computing bond price and bond yield are ones commonly used in practice. However, be aware of the fact that the examples shown are specific illustrations and do not take into account all of the factors that may affect the bond market. Historically, bond transactions have incorporated a variety of approximations, and many different types of calculations are still in use today. Because of this, the answers using the following methods may not agree exactly with answers you get from other sources.

References:

Farish, et al, *Calculator Analysis for Business and Finance,* Chapter 5.

Greynolds, Aronofsky, and Frame, *Financial Analysis Using Calculators: Time Value of Money,* pp. 335-347.

Spence, Graudenz, and Lynch, *Standard Securities Calculation Methods.*

Determining Purchase Price of a Bond Sold on an Interest Date (More Than One Coupon Payment Left)

You're considering the purchase of a commercial bond as an investment. Let's say that you want any bond that you purchase and hold to maturity to yield 7% interest compounded semiannually. Otherwise, you won't invest. If the par value is $1000, how much should you pay for a 4% semiannual bond which matures in 6 years?

The total price is the sum of the present value of the bond redeemed at par (steps 3 through 6) and the present value of the coupon payments (steps 7 and 8).

Procedure	Press		Display
1. Clear calculator and mode registers; select two decimal places.	[ON/C] [STO] [2nd] [CMR] [FIX] 2		**0.00**
2. Select financial mode ("FIN" shows in the display).	[2nd] [Mode]	FIN	**0.00**
3. Calculate and enter number of coupon payments.	6 [×] 2 [=] [N]	FIN	**12.00**
4. Calculate and enter required periodic interest rate (yield per coupon period).	7 [÷] 2 [=] [%i]	FIN	**3.50**
5. Enter face value of bond.	1000 [FV]	FIN	**1000.00**
6. Compute and store present value of bond's redemption value.	[2nd] [PV] [STO]	FIN	**661.78**
7. Calculate and enter amount of coupon payments.	4 [%] [÷] 2 [×] 1000 [=] [PMT]	FIN	**20.00**
8. Compute present value of payments and add to memory.	[2nd] [PV] [SUM]	FIN	**193.27**
9. Recall bond price.	[RCL]	FIN	**855.05**

The maximum purchase price of the bond is $855.05. Note that if you can buy the bond for less, your yield will be higher. If you have to pay more, your yield will be lower than your desired rate.

Determining Purchase Price of a Bond Sold between Interest Dates (More Than One Coupon Payment Left)

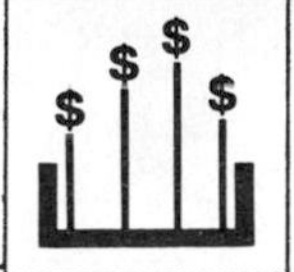

A semiannual bond with 183 days in the current coupon period is sold during the period (106 days after the previous coupon payment), and 33 coupon payments remain. The bond's par value is $1000 with a nominal interest rate of 7%. If the bond's yield should be 8%, what is the bond's price, both before and after the accrued interest is deducted? (With this procedure, the bond's value should be entered in "points." In other words, a $1000 bond equals 100.)

The time line for the situation is:

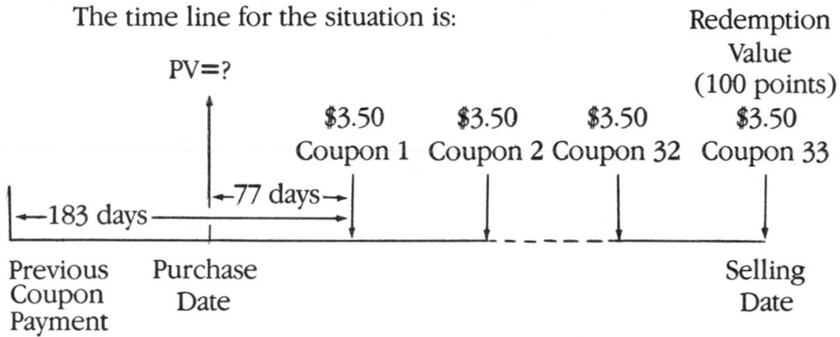

The bond's price at the settlement date can be calculated as follows:

1. Add the present value of the redemption value on the next coupon date (steps 3 through 6) and the present value of the coupon payments on the next coupon date (steps 7 through 10).
2. Compute the present value of the previous sum as of the settlement date (steps 12 and 13).
3. Subtract the accrued interest from the computed present value (steps 14 and 15).

(continued on next page)

Determining Purchase Price of a Bond Sold between Interest Dates (More Than One Coupon Payment Left)

Procedure	Press		Display
1. Clear calculator and mode registers; select two decimal places.	[ON/C] [STO] [2nd] [CMR] [FIX] 2		0.00
2. Select financial mode ("FIN" shows in the display).	[2nd] [Mode]	FIN	0.00
3. Subtract 1 (one) from number of remaining coupon payments and enter result.	33 [−] 1 [=] [N]	FIN	32.00
4. Calculate and enter periodic yield.	8 [÷] 2 [=] [%i]	FIN	4.00
5. Enter par or redemption value (in points).	100 [FV]	FIN	100.00
6. Compute and store present value.	[2nd] [PV] [STO]	FIN	28.51
7. Calculate periodic nominal interest rate.	7 [%] [÷] 2 [=]	FIN	0.04
8. Multiply by par value in points to calculate amount of coupon payments.	[×] 100 [=] [PMT]	FIN	3.50
9. Compute present value of coupon payments.	[2nd] [PV]	FIN	62.56
10. Add amount of coupon payments (step 8).	[+] 3.50 [=]	FIN	66.06

Determining Purchase Price of a Bond Sold between Interest Dates (More Than One Coupon Payment Left)

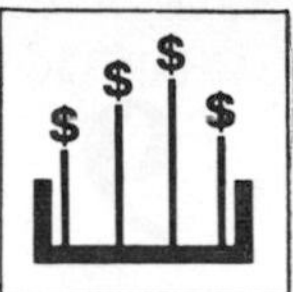

Procedure	Press		Display
11. Add displayed value to present value of redemption value stored in memory (step 6).	[SUM]	FIN	**66.06**
12. Calculate and enter portion of coupon period remaining (number of days in coupon period − accrued interest days ÷ number of days in period).	183 [−] 106 [÷] 183 [=] [N]	FIN	**0.42**
13. Compute and store present value of bond at settlement date, including accrued interest.	0 [PMT]	FIN	**0.00**
	[RCL] [FV]	FIN	**94.56**
	[2nd] [PV] [STO]	FIN	**93.02**
14. Calculate amount of accrued interest due seller (amount of coupon payment × accrued interest days ÷ number of days in period).	3.5 [×] 106 [÷] 183 [=]	FIN	**2.03**
15. Subtract accrued interest (step 14) from bond value (step 13) to calculate bond value, excluding accrued interest.	[+/−] [+] [RCL] [=]	FIN	**90.99**

The bond's price is 93.02 per $100 before the accrued interest is deducted and 90.99 per $100 after the interest is deducted.

CHAPTER 9

Determining Purchase Price of a Bond Sold Between Interest Dates (One Coupon Payment Left)

You purchase a $1000 bond, with one remaining coupon payment, 145 days after the previous payment. Since there are 183 days in the current coupon period, 38 days remain until maturity (183 −145). The bond's nominal annual interest rate is 9% with semiannual coupon payments. If the final coupon payment is made at redemption, and you want the bond to yield 12%, what is the purchase price? (When you use this solution procedure, the value of the bond should be stated in points, $1000 equals 100 points.)

The problem can be solved as follows:

1. Discount the sum of the bond's redemption value and the final coupon payment to the purchase date (steps 2 through 7). (In this case, the interest is not compounded since the bond is to be held for less than six months.)
2. Subtract the accrued interest due the seller to determine the bond price (steps 8 through 11).

Procedure	Press	Display
1. Clear calculator and select two decimal places.	[ON/C] [STO] [FIX] 2	**0.00**
2. Divide redemption value by 100 and store result.	100 [÷] 100 [=] [STO]	**1.00**
3. Calculate periodic interest rate (annual rate ÷ number of payments per year).	9 [%] [÷] 2 [=]	**0.05**
4. Add step 2 value and store result.	[+] [RCL] [=] [STO]	**1.05**
5. Enter number of days until coupon payment and divide by number of days in coupon period.	38 [÷] 183 [=]	**0.21**
6. Multiply by yield, divide by number of coupon payments per year, and add 1 (one).	[×] 12 [%] [÷] 2 [+] 1 [=]	**1.01**

Determining Purchase Price of a Bond Sold Between Interest Dates (One Coupon Payment Left)

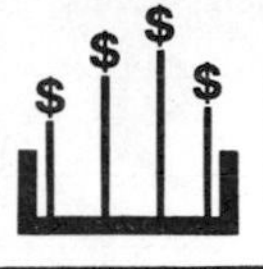

Procedure	Press	Display
7. Divide value in memory (step 4) by result of step 6 to calculate and store bond price per dollar, including accrued interest.	[EXC] [÷] [RCL] [=] [STO]	1.03
8. Enter number of accrued interest days and divide by number of days in coupon period.	145 [÷] 183 [=]	0.79
9. Multiply by annual interest rate and divide by number of coupon payments per year to calculate accrued interest per dollar.	[×] 9 [%] [÷] 2 [=]	0.04
10. Subtract accrued interest (step 9) from bond price (step 7) to calculate price of bond per dollar without accrued interest.	[+/−] [+] [RCL] [=]	1.00
11. Multiply by 100 to calculate price of bond per $100.	[×] 100 [=]	**99.65**

To yield 12%, the purchase price of the bond should be 99.65 per $100.

See *Appendix A* for the formula.

CHAPTER 9 Finding Yield to Maturity on a Commercial Bond Purchased on an Interest Date

A 4% $1000 semiannual bond that matures in 6 years is quoted at $85 1/4, which means you could buy it for $852.50 (ignoring commissions). At this price, what is your yield to maturity?

Since the equation cannot directly solve for the interest rate, the solution must be found through a repetitive, trial-and-error process known as an iteration. See steps 6 through 12.

Procedure	Press		Display
1. Clear calculator and mode registers; select two decimal places.	[ON/C] [STO] [2nd] [CMR] [FIX] 2		**0.00**
2. Select financial mode ("FIN" shows in the display).	[2nd] [Mode]	FIN	**0.00**
3. Calculate and enter number of coupon payments.	6 [×] 2 [=] [N]	FIN	**12.00**
4. Calculate amount of coupon payment.	4 [%] [÷] 2 [×] 1000 [=]	FIN	**20.00**
5. Store purchase price of bond.	852.50 [STO]	FIN	**852.50**
6. Calculate future value (redemption value of bond − purchase price ÷ purchase price × 100).	1000 [−] [RCL] [÷] [RCL] [×] 100 [=] [FV]	FIN	**17.30**

Finding Yield to Maturity on a Commercial Bond Purchased on an Interest Date

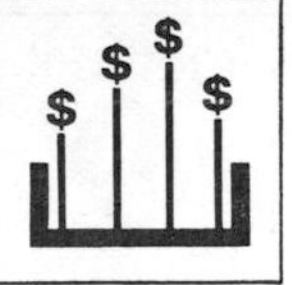

Procedure	Press		Display
7. Calculate and store (amount of coupon payment ÷ purchase price × 100).	20 [÷] [RCL] [×] 100 [=] [STO]	FIN	**2.35**
8. Enter first estimate for %i (step 6 value or your own estimate).	[%i]	FIN	**2.35**
9. Calculate second estimate for %i.	[2nd] [PMT] [+] [RCL] [=] [%i]	FIN	**3.61**
10. Calculate third estimate.	[2nd] [PMT] [+] [RCL] [=] [%i]	FIN	**3.52**
11. Calculate fourth estimate.	[2nd] [PMT] [+] [RCL] [=] [%i]	FIN	**3.53**
12. Calculate fifth estimate.*	[2nd] [PMT] [+] [RCL] [=] [%i]	FIN	**3.53**
13. Multiply by number of periods per year to calculate annual yield to maturity.	[×] 2 [=]	FIN	**7.06**

You'll earn 7.06% annual interest, compounded semiannually, if you purchase the bond.

*To find the yield with this procedure, repeat the key sequence for estimating the interest rate (steps 9 through 12) until the displayed answer equals the previous answer or until the answer reaches your desired level of accuracy. Notice that, in this case, the fifth estimate equals the fourth estimate so the iteration is complete in step 12. You might want to display more decimal places to increase the level of accuracy.

CHAPTER

9 Amortizing a Bond Premium or Discount (Effective Interest Method)

The LB Tennis Ranch has issued $100,000 worth of bonds for $93,204.84. The bonds mature in ten years and have a nominal rate of 7% with a semiannual coupon. The annual yield to maturity is 8%, or 4% per coupon period. Calculate the bond discount, amortized interest, and balance for periods 1 and 2.

Procedure	Press	Display
1. Clear calculator and select two decimal places.	[ON/C] [STO] [FIX] 2	**0.00**
2. Calculate amount of coupon payment (nominal rate ÷ number of payments per year × bond value).	7 [%] [÷] 2 [×] 100000 [=]	**3500.00**
3. Store cost of bonds.	93204.84 [STO]	**93204.84**
4. Multiply by yield per coupon period to calculate bond interest expense for period 1.	[×] 4 [%] [=]	**3728.19**

Amortizing a Bond Premium or Discount (Effective Interest Method)

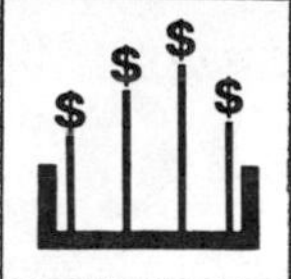

Procedure	Press	Display
5. Subtract coupon payment amount (step 2) to calculate discount (premium) amortized for period 1 and add to memory.	[−] 3500 [=] [SUM]	**228.19**
6. Recall value in memory to display adjusted book value (balance) at end of period 1.	[RCL]	**93433.03**
7. Multiply by yield per coupon period to calculate bond interest expense for period 2.	[×] 4 [%] [=]	**3737.32**
8. Subtract coupon payment amount (step 2) to calculate discount for period 2.	[−] 3500 [=] [SUM]	**237.32**

Repeat steps 5 through 7 for each period.

Reference:

Kieso and Weygandt, *Intermediate Accounting,* pp. 560-562.

CHAPTER **10**

NET PRESENT VALUE AND RATES OF RETURN

You can use a variety of time-value-of-money techniques to evaluate long term investments involving a series of cash flows. The four techniques discussed here are Net Present Value (NPV), Internal Rate of Return (IRR), return on funds reinvested at the required return rate, and modified Financial Management Rate of Return (FMRR).

NPV is the present value of a project's after-tax cash flows, less the outlay cash cost.

The IRR routine finds the interest rate which equates the present value of the cash flows with the outlay cost, assuming that the cash flows are reinvested at the IRR. If negative cash flows occur among a series of positive cash flows, you can get multiple IRR answers (which are usually invalid).

The method for finding the return on funds reinvested at the required rate assumes that the cash flows are compounded forward at the required return rate to the end of the decision period. The interest rate which discounts the future value to an amount equal to the present value is the return.

The modified FMRR method can be used instead of the IRR routine when multiple negative cash flows are present. This method assumes that positive cash flows can be reinvested at your company's cost-of-capital rate. Any negative cash flows are discounted at a safe or sure interest rate, such as the rate on a savings account. Thus, the total present value of the negative cash flows represents the amount to be funded at the "safe" interest rate at the beginning of the project. The positive cash flows are compounded forward at the cost-of-capital rate to determine their future value. The modified FMRR is the interest rate which discounts the future value to an amount equal to the present value.

With your calculator you can quickly apply these techniques to long term investment situations.

Finding the Modified Financial Management Rate of Return

A company is evaluating a $5000 investment with a five-year life and after-tax cash flows of:

Year	1	2	3	4	5
Cash Flow	3500	−2500	3800	−3300	14500

The project has a net present value of $351.08 with a 20% required earnings rate. If the negative cash flows are funded by investing in a savings account which pays 5.5%, what is the modified financial management rate of return (FMRR)?

The amount necessary to fund the negative cash flows is the sum of the present value of those cash flows.

The example can be represented on a time line as:

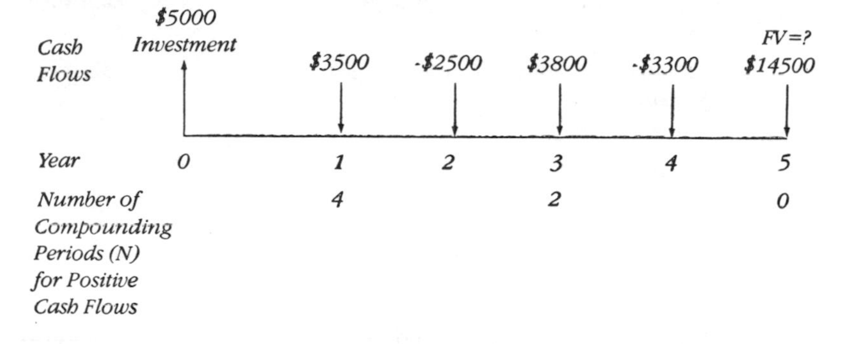

(continued on next page)

Finding the Modified Financial Management Rate of Return

	Procedure	Press		Display
1.	Clear calculator and mode registers; select two decimal places.	ON/C STO 2nd CMR FIX 2		**0.00**
2.	Select financial mode ("FIN" shows in the display).	2nd Mode	FIN	**0.00**
3.	Enter "safe" interest rate.	5.5 %i	FIN	**5.50**
4.	Enter period of first negative cash flow.	2 N	FIN	**2.00**
5.	Enter amount of negative cash flow.	2500 FV	FIN	**2500.00**
6.	Compute present value of negative cash flow and store result.	2nd PV STO	FIN	**2246.13**
7.	**Repeat Steps 4-6 for each negative cash flow.**			
a.	Enter period of next negative cash flow.	4 N	FIN	**4.00**
b.	Enter amount of negative cash flow.	3300 FV	FIN	**3300.00**
c.	Compute present value of negative cash flow and add to memory.	2nd PV SUM	FIN	**2663.82**

Finding the Modified Financial Management Rate of Return

Procedure	Press		Display
8. Recall total present value of negative cash flows.	[RCL]	FIN	**4909.95**
9. Add initial cash outlay to calculate total present value.	[+] 5000 [=]	FIN	**9909.95**
10. Enter required interest rate.	20 [%i]	FIN	**20.00**
11. Compute future value of positive cash flows.			
a. Period 1	4 [N]	FIN	**4.00**
	3500 [PV]	FIN	**3500.00**
	[2nd] [FV] [STO]	FIN	**7257.60**
b. Period 3	2 [N]	FIN	**2.00**
	3800 [PV]	FIN	**3800.00**
	[2nd] [FV] [SUM]	FIN	**5472.00**
c. Add period 5 cash flow.	14500 [SUM]	FIN	**14500.00**
12. Recall total future value of cash flows and enter as future value.	[RCL] [FV]	FIN	**27229.60**
13. Enter number of periods (years).	5 [N]	FIN	**5.00**
14. Enter present value from step 9.	9909.95 [PV]	FIN	**9909.95**
15. Compute modified FMRR.	[2nd] [%i]	FIN	**22.40**

The modified FMRR is 22.40% which exceeds the required return rate of 20%.

CHAPTER 10 A Simple Example of Net Present Value and Rates of Return, Excluding Taxes

The Enterprise Paper Company is planning to pay $19,600 for a production machine which should save the company $5000 a year for the next 10 years. The new machine will replace a current machine which has a zero market value. Enterprise requires a return rate of 20% on investments of this type. Excluding taxes and assuming a zero salvage value, find (a) the net present value of the new machine, (b) the internal rate of return, and (c) the return if the savings are reinvested at 20%. (Assume that all cash flows occur at the end of each year.)

Procedure	Press		Display
1. Clear calculator and mode registers; select two decimal places.	ON/C 2nd CMR FIX 2		0.00
2. Select financial mode ("FIN" shows in the display).	2nd Mode	FIN	0.00

A. Finding the net present value.

Procedure	Press		Display
3. Enter number of periods (years).	10 N	FIN	10.00
4. Enter required return rate.	20 %i	FIN	20.00
5. Enter amount of annual savings.	5000 PMT	FIN	5000.00
6. Compute present value.	2nd PV	FIN	20962.36
7. Subtract cost of machine to calculate net present value.	− 19600 =	FIN	1362.36

B. Finding the internal rate of return.

Procedure	Press		Display
8. Enter initial cash outlay.	19600 [PV]	FIN	**19600.00**
9. Compute internal rate of return.	[2nd] [%i]	FIN	**22.03**

C. Finding the return on funds reinvested at the required return rate.

Procedure	Press		Display
10. Enter reinvestment rate.	20 [%i]	FIN	**20.00**
11. Enter amount of payment.	5000 [PMT]	FIN	**5000.00**
12. Compute future value.	[2nd] [FV]	FIN	**129793.41**
13. Enter 0 (zero) for payment.	0 [PMT]	FIN	**0.00**
14. Enter initial cash outlay.	19600 [PV]	FIN	**19600.00**
15. Compute return if savings are reinvested at required earnings rate.	[2nd] [%i]	FIN	**20.81**

The net present value of the proposed purchase is $1362.36. The internal rate of return is 22.03%, assuming that the cash flows are reinvested at the same rate. If the cash flows are reinvested at 20%, the return rate is 20.81%.

CHAPTER 10	Finding Net Present Value, Reinvestment Return, and IRR with Equal Cash Flows and Straight-Line Depreciation

Your company is considering the purchase of a $900,000 depreciable asset having a 10-year life. For depreciation purposes, the salvage value of the asset is $50,000, but your company expects to sell it for $75,000 at the end of 10 years. The annual cash inflows before taxes and depreciation total $385,000. The tax rate on the operating income is estimated at 40%, and the tax rate on the gain when the asset is sold is 16%. If your company requires an 18% annual return rate on this investment, find (a) the net present value of the asset, (b) the return rate if the cash flows are reinvested at 18%, and (c) the IRR. (Assume that all cash flows occur at the end of each year.)

Procedure	Press		Display
1. Clear calculator and mode registers; select two decimal places.	[ON/C] [STO] [2nd] [CMR] [FIX] 2		**0.00**
2. Select financial mode ("FIN" shows in the display).	[2nd] [Mode]	FIN	**0.00**

A. Finding the net present value.

Procedure	Press		Display
3. Enter number of periods.	10 [N]	FIN	**10.00**
4. Enter required return rate.	18 [%i]	FIN	**18.00**
5. Calculate capital gains taxable income (sale value − salvage value).	75000 [−] 50000 [=]	FIN	**25000.00**
6. Multiply by tax rate on gain to calculate amount of tax liability.	[×] 16 [%] [=]	FIN	**4000.00**
7. Subtract tax liability from future sales price to calculate after-tax cash flow from sale of asset.	[+/−] [+] 75000 [=] [FV]	FIN	**71000.00**

Finding Net Present Value, Reinvestment Return, and IRR with Equal Cash Flows and Straight-Line Depreciation

Procedure	Press		Display
8. Compute and store present value of cash flow from sale of asset.	[2nd] [PV] [STO]	FIN	**13565.58**
9. Calculate annual straight-line depreciation (cost − salvage value ÷ life of asset).	900000 [−] 50000 [÷] 10 [=]	FIN	**85000.00**
10. Calculate taxable income (annual cash flow before taxes − depreciation).	[+/−] [+] 385000 [=]	FIN	**300000.00**
11. Multiply by tax rate on income to calculate tax liability.	[×] 40 [%] [=]	FIN	**120000.00**
12. Calculate after-tax cash flow (annual cash flow before taxes − tax liability).	[+/−] [+] 385000 [=]	FIN	**265000.00**
13. Enter after-tax cash flow as payment amount.	[PMT]	FIN	**265000.00**
14. Compute present value of after-tax cash flows and add to present value of sale of asset (step 8).	[2nd] [PV] [SUM]	FIN	**1190932.9**
15. Recall total of present values of cash flow and sale of asset.	[RCL]	FIN	**1204498.4**
16. Subtract initial cash outlay to determine net present value.	[−] 900000 [=]	FIN	**304498.45**

(continued on next page)

B. Finding the reutrn on funds reinvested at the required return rate.

	Procedure	Press		Display
17.	Compute future value of after-tax cash flows.	[2nd] [FV]	FIN	**6233146.8**
18.	Add after-tax cash flow from sale of asset (step 7).	[+] 71000 [=] [FV]	FIN	**6304146.8**
19.	Enter 0 (zero) for payment.	0 [PMT]	FIN	**0.00**
20.	Enter initial cash outlay.	900000 [PV]	FIN	**900000.00**
21.	**Compute return if cash flows are reinvested at required earnings rate.**	[2nd] [%i]	FIN	**21.49**

C. Finding the internal rate of return.

	Procedure	Press		Display
22.	Store initial cash outlay.	900000 [STO]	FIN	**900000.00**
23.	Calculate future value (cash flow from sale of asset − initial cash outlay ÷ initial cash outlay × 100).	71000 [−] [RCL] [÷] [RCL] [×] 100 [=] [FV]	FIN	**-92.11**

Finding Net Present Value, Reinvestment Return, and IRR with Equal Cash Flows and Straight-Line Depreciation

Procedure	Press		Display
24. Calculate and store (after-tax cash flow from step 12 ÷ initial cash outlay × 100).	265000 [÷] [RCL] [X] 100 [=] [STO]	FIN	**29.44**
25. Enter first estimate for %i (step 24 value or your own estimate).	[%i]	FIN	**29.44**
26. Calculate second estimate.	[2nd] [PMT] [+] [RCL] [=] [%i]	FIN	**27.22**
27. Calculate third estimate.	[2nd] [PMT] [+] [RCL] [=] [%i]	FIN	**26.96**
28. Calculate fourth estimate.	[2nd] [PMT] [+] [RCL] [=] [%i]	FIN	**26.93**
29. Calculate fifth estimate.*	[2nd] [PMT] [+] [RCL] [=] [%i]	FIN	**26.93**

This investment has a net present value of $304,498.45. The return rate is 21.49% if the after-tax cash flows are reinvested at 18% and 26.93% if reinvested at the IRR.

*To find the return rate with this procedure, repeat the key sequence for estimating the interest rate (steps 26 through 29) until the displayed answer equals the previous answer or until the answer reaches your desired level of accuracy. Notice that in this case, the fifth estimate equals the fourth estimate so the iteration is complete in step 29. You might want to display more decimal places to increase the level of accuracy.

CHAPTER 10 Determining Net Present Value and Rate of Return with Variable Cash Flows and Accelerated Depreciation

You are evaluating an investment in a $60,000 depreciable asset with an eight-year life. The asset has a $10,000 salvage value for depreciation purposes but will probably sell for $4000 at the end of eight years. The asset will be depreciated by the declining balance method with a factor of 200%. The operating cash flows before taxes and the depreciation for each year are:

Year	1	2	3	4	5	6	7	8
Operating Cash Flows	14000	22000	27000	34000	43000	39000	37000	30000
*Depreciation**	15000	11250	8437.50	6328.13	4746.09	3559.57	678.71	0

With a tax rate of 45%, each cash flow is multiplied by 55% (100% − 45%) to determine the after-tax operating cash flows. The yearly depreciation is multiplied by 45% to obtain the tax benefit from depreciation. The results of these calculations are:

Year	1	2	3	4	5	6	7	8
After-tax Operating Cash Flows	7700.00	12100.00	14850.00	18700.00	23650.00	21450.00	20350.00	16500.00
Tax Benefit from Depreciation	6750.00	5062.00	3796.88	2847.66	2135.74	1601.81	305.42	0.00
TOTAL	14450.00	17162.50	18646.88	21547.66	25785.74	23051.81	20655.42	16500.00

The tax rate on the gain or loss resulting from the sale of asset is 18%, and you require a return of 22% on this project. What are (a) the net present value and (b) the return rate if the cash flows are reinvested at 22%?

*The model assumes that any operating losses will represent a tax savings on other taxable income.

Determining Net Present Value and Rate of Return with Variable Cash Flows and Accelerated Depreciation

	Procedure	Press		Display
1.	Clear calculator and mode registers; select two decimal places.	[ON/C] [STO] [2nd] [CMR] [FIX] 2		0.00
2.	Select financial mode ("FIN" shows in the display).	[2nd] [Mode]	FIN	0.00
A. Finding the net present value.				
3.	Enter number of periods.	8 [N]	FIN	8.00
4.	Enter required return rate.	22 [%i]	FIN	22.00
5.	Enter proceeds from sale of asset and subtract salvage value.	4000 [−] 10000 [=]	FIN	-6000.00
6.	Multiply by tax rate on sale of asset to calculate amount of tax liability.	[×] 18 [%] [=]	FIN	-1080.00
7.	Subtract tax liability from future sales price to calculate after-tax cash flow from sale of asset.	[+/−] [+] 4000 [=] [FV]	FIN	5080.00
8.	Compute present value of cash flow from sale of asset.	[2nd] [PV]	FIN	1035.11

(continued on next page)

	Procedure	Press		Display
9.	**Compute present value of after-tax cash flows, using sum of cash flows and depreciaton as future value.**			
a.	Period 1	1 [N]	FIN	**1.00**
		14450 [FV]	FIN	**14450.00**
		[2nd] [PV] [STO]	FIN	**11844.26**
b.	Period 2	2 [N]	FIN	**2.00**
		17162.50 [FV]	FIN	**17162.50**
		[2nd] [PV] [SUM]	FIN	**11530.84**
c.	Period 3	3 [N]	FIN	**3.00**
		18646.88 [FV]	FIN	**18646.88**
		[2nd] [PV] [SUM]	FIN	**10268.97**
d.	Period 4	4 [N]	FIN	**4.00**
		21547.66 [FV]	FIN	**21547.66**
		[2nd] [PV] [SUM]	FIN	**9726.59**
e.	Period 5	5 [N]	FIN	**5.00**
		25785.74 [FV]	FIN	**25785.74**
		[2nd] [PV] [SUM]	FIN	**9540.70**
f.	Period 6	6 [N]	FIN	**6.00**
		23051.81 [FV]	FIN	**23051.81**
		[2nd] [PV] [SUM]	FIN	**6991.11**
g.	Period 7	7 [N]	FIN	**7.00**
		20655.42 [FV]	FIN	**20655.42**
		[2nd] [PV] [SUM]	FIN	**5134.70**
h.	Period 8	8 [N]	FIN	**8.00**
		16500 [FV]	FIN	**16500.00**
		[2nd] [PV] [SUM]	FIN	**3362.06**
10.	Recall total present value of after-tax cash flows.	[RCL]	FIN	**68399.23**

Procedure	Press		Display
11. Add cash flow from sale of asset (step 8); store result.	[+] 1035.11 [=] [STO]	FIN	**69434.34**
12. Subtract initial cash outlay to calculate net present value.	[−] 60000 [=]	FIN	**9434.34**

B. Finding the return on funds reinvested at the required return rate.

Procedure	Press		Display
13. Enter number of periods.	8 [N]	FIN	**8.00**
14. Enter 0 (zero) for payment.	0 [PMT]	FIN	**0.00**
15. Recall total present value (step 11).	[RCL] [PV]	FIN	**69434.34**
16. Compute future value.	[2nd] [FV]	FIN	**340763.43**
17. Enter initial cash outlay.	60000 [PV]	FIN	**60000.00**
18. Compute return if cash flows are reinvested at required earnings rate.	[2nd] [%i]	FIN	**24.25**

The net present value of this investment is $9434.34, and the return rate is 24.25% if the cash flows are reinvested at 22%.

To find the IRR, enter various guesses for %i. Since the net present value in this example is positive, the IRR is probably higher than 22%. Therefore, you could enter 30% as the rate in step 4 and repeat steps 5-12. Repeat this procedure, as necessary, until the net present value is close to zero.

CHAPTER

11 STATISTICS

Whether you need to analyze the volume of sales in a store, project overhead expenses, or forecast the possible effects of advertising on income, the statistics branch of mathematics can be an invaluable aid. However, performing the calculations can be a lengthy and time-consuming process. The statistical keys on your calculator can help you quickly perform the complex computations, leaving you with more time to analyze the results.

This chapter illustrates some of the most common business applications of statistics. Select the example which fits your needs, and then enter your values instead of those in the example.

There are basically two types of statistics. One is descriptive statistics, which involves collecting, grouping, and presenting large sets of data in ways that can be easily understood or assimilated. The other kind, inductive statistics or statistical inference, is used to draw conclusions from your observed data — to estimate population parameters from sample data, for example, and/or to predict trends and explore probabilities.

For problems involving descriptive statistics, several statistical calculations are used to "describe" the characteristics of the data set. One of the most common is finding the *mean,* or average, of the data. When you press [2nd] [Mean], the calculator computes the mean of your data (the sum of the values divided by the number of values).

Standard deviation, or the "spread" (distribution) of your data points, is another frequently calculated descriptive statistic. Your calculator has two standard deviation keys, [2nd] [σn] and [2nd] [σn-1]. [2nd] [σn] is used to calculate the standard deviation of a *population* (a complete data set). Pressing [2nd] [σn-1] calculates an estimated standard deviation based on a *sample* (a set of elements selected randomly to represent a population).

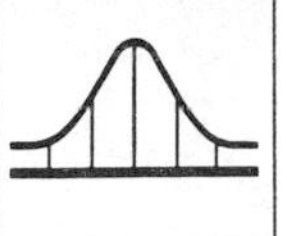

The difference between the two keys is in the *weighting* given by the *n* factor used in the calculations (n is the number of elements in the population or sample). When your data set represents a whole population, press [2nd] [σn] to calculate the standard deviation using *n weighting* (dividing by the number of elements in the population). With sample data, press [2nd] [σn-1] to estimate the standard deviation of the whole population with *n-1 weighting* (dividing by the number of elements in the sample minus one). *Note:* The difference between the *estimated standard deviation* (based on a sample) and the *population standard deviation* becomes very small for over 30 sample data points.

One of the inferential statistical procedures illustrated in this chapter is *linear regression.* In linear regression, you usually have data expressed as pairs of variables (x,y) that you could plot on a graph. The calculator mathematically draws a straight-line graph through the set of data points. The actual placement of the line is determined by a least squares linear regression that minimizes the sum of the squares of the deviation of the y values from the straight line of best fit. The equation is in the form

$$y=ax+b$$

where a is the slope of the line and b is the y-intercept (where the line crosses the y-axis).

In most instances, the x variable is considered the independent variable, while y is the dependent variable. The relationship between the two sets of variables (x and y), as defined by the equation, can be used to find the slope, y-intercept, and correlation coefficient. The correlation coefficient ([2nd] [Corr]) tells you how well the line "fits" the data. The closer the value is to ± 1, the better the fit.

NOTE: It is not statistically valid to compute an x (independent) value on the basis of a y (dependent) value or to compute a y value on the basis of an x which is outside the range of entered x values. However, trend line analysis and forecasting calculations often use these computations to make *predictions* or *estimations of probability* about the future. When you perform such calculations, it's important to remember that the actual values may differ from the calculated values, which only indicate what could happen based on the data you've entered.

Finding the Mean, Standard Deviation, and Standard Error of Mean for a Sample

Your company has 40 small retail stores located throughout the state. From these stores, you decide to compare the average daily sales of Store A, which is located in the western part of state, with Store B in the eastern part. Although each store is open 259 days a year, you select the following random sample of 20 days for each store's sales.

Day	Store A (x)	Store B (y)
1	650	600
2	625	660
3	600	700
4	675	670
5	650	620
6	625	580
7	610	630
8	590	570
9	580	600
10	595	690
11	630	640
12	610	560
13	640	500
14	620	575
15	635	640
16	620	650
17	615	680
18	605	720
19	625	620
20	610	580

Based on the sample data, you want to estimate the average daily sales and the standard deviation of the sales for each store.

Procedure	Press		Display
1. Clear calculator and mode registers; select two decimal places.	ON/C 2nd CMR FIX 2		**0.00**
2. Select statistical mode ("STAT" shows in the display).	2nd Mode	STAT	**0.00**

Finding the Mean, Standard Deviation, and Standard Error of Mean for a Sample

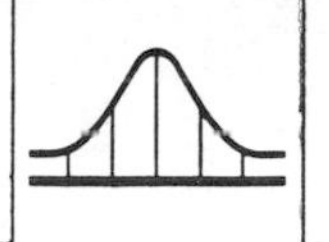

Procedure	Press		Display
3. Enter data. (Calculator displays current number of data entries.)			
a. Enter first x value (Store A).	650 [x:y]	STAT	**0.00**
Enter first y value (Store B).	600 [Σ+]	STAT	**1.00**
b. Enter second pair of data points.	625 [x:y] 660 [Σ+]	STAT	**2.00**
c. Enter third pair of data points.	600 [x:y] 700 [Σ+]	STAT	**3.00**
d. Continue to enter remaining values as above.	⋮		⋮
e. Enter nineteenth pair of data points.	625 [x:y] 620 [Σ+]	STAT	**19.00**
f. Enter twentieth pair of data points.	610 [x:y] 580 [Σ+]	STAT	**20.00**
4. Compute mean of y value (Store B).	[2nd] [Mean]	STAT	**624.25**
5. Display mean of x value (Store A).	[x:y]	STAT	**620.50**
6. Compute estimate of sales variation (standard deviation) for y value (Store B).	[2nd] [σ_{n-1}]	STAT	**54.75**
7. Display estimate of sales variation (standard deviation) for x value (Store A).	[x:y]	STAT	**22.59**

For this sample, the average daily sales of $620.50 for Store A and $624.25 for Store B are similar. However, the estimated standard deviations of $22.59 for Store A and $54.75 for Store B indicate that Store B's sales vary more than Store A's do.

Notice that when you are working with two-variable data, x is entered before y. After the calculations are completed, the calculator displays the result for the y value first.

Finding the Mean, Standard Deviation, and Variance of a Population

The company's personnel department has recently given an office skills test to the five members of your clerical staff. The test scores are in now, and you'd like to analyze the data to see how well your staff did. The scores were 4, 5, 6, 7, and 8, out of a possible score of 10.

With your calculator you can easily calculate the mean, the standard deviation, and the variance.

Procedure	Press		Display
1. Clear calculator and mode registers; select two decimal places.	[ON/C] [2nd] [CMR] [FIX] 2		**0.00**
2. Select statistical mode ("STAT" shows in the display).	[2nd] [Mode]	STAT	**0.00**
3. Enter data. (Calculator displays current number of data entries.)	4 [Σ+]	STAT	**1.00**
	5 [Σ+]	STAT	**2.00**
	6 [Σ+]	STAT	**3.00**
	7 [Σ+]	STAT	**4.00**
	8 [Σ+]	STAT	**5.00**
4. Compute mean.	[2nd] [Mean]	STAT	**6.00**
5. Compute standard deviation.	[2nd] [σn]	STAT	**1.41**
6. Calculate variance.	[x^2]	STAT	**2.00**

The average score is 6, and the standard deviation is 1.41. This means that the majority of your test scores fall within the range of 6 ± 1.41. The variance (the square of the standard deviation) is 2.

Notice that the key sequence [2nd] [σn] is used to find the standard deviation with n weighting because the calculations involve the entire population (your clerical staff).

Estimating Costs with Linear Regression Analysis

You have determined that as the number of direct labor hours increases, your company's overhead manufacturing costs also increase. You would like to predict the total overhead costs and the variable overhead costs within the normal production range of 4000 to 6000 hours. The following data is a sample of the number of labor hours worked and the actual manufacturing overhead incurred for the last 12 months.

Month	Direct Labor Hours (x)	Manufacturing Overhead ($y)
1	4000	21,050
2	4500	24,010
3	5000	24,800
4	5200	25,820
5	5600	26,730
6	6000	28,150
7	5500	26,585
8	4900	24,640
9	4700	24,030
10	4500	23,595
11	4400	23,104
12	4200	22,440

With this data set, you can develop an overhead cost equation, determine the variable overhead rate per hour, and estimate the total overhead for 5400 hours of direct labor.

In addition, you can evaluate the accuracy of the cost equation by calculating the correlation coefficient, the index of determination, the standard error of the equation, and the standard error of the variable overhead rate estimate.

Procedure	Press		Display
1. Clear calculator and mode registers; select two decimal places.	[ON/C] [STO] [2nd] [CMR] [FIX] 2		**0.00**
2. Select statistical mode ("STAT" shows in the display).	[2nd] [Mode]	STAT	**0.00**

(continued on next page)

Procedure	Press		Display
3. Enter data. (Calculator displays current number of data entries.)			
a. Enter first x value.	4000 [x:y]	STAT	**0.00**
Enter first y value.	21050 [Σ+]	STAT	**1.00**
b. Enter second pair of data points.	4500 [x:y] 24010 [Σ+]	STAT	**2.00**
c. Enter third pair of data points.	5000 [x:y] 24800 [Σ+]	STAT	**3.00**
d. Continue to enter remaining values as above.	. . .		. . .
e. Enter eleventh pair of data points.	4400 [x:y] 23104 [Σ+]	STAT	**11.00**
f. Enter twelfth pair of data points.	4200 [x:y] 22440 [Σ+]	STAT	**12.00**
4. Compute y-intercept of regression line.	[2nd] [b/a]	STAT	**8770.88**
5. Display slope of regression line (variable overhead rate).	[x:y]	STAT	**3.24**
6. Compute correlation coefficient.	[2nd] [Corr]	STAT	**0.99**
7. Calculate and store index of determination.	[x²] [STO]	STAT	**0.98**
8. Calculate standard error of regression line, using number of pairs of points entered previously.*	1 [−] [RCL] [=] [STO]	STAT	**0.02**
	[2nd] [σn] [x²] [×]		
	[RCL] [=] [STO]	STAT	**89470.27**
	12 [EXC] [×] [RCL] [=]	STAT	**1073643.2**
	[EXC] [−] 2 [=]	STAT	**10.00**
	[1/x] [×] [RCL] [=]		
	[2nd] [√x] [STO]	STAT	**327.66**

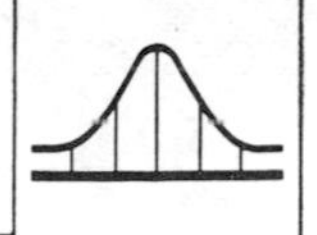

Procedure	Press		Display
9. Calculate standard error of slope, using number of pairs of points entered previously.*	[2nd] [σn] [$x:y$]		
	[x^2]	STAT	**338541.67**
	[×] 12 [=] [2nd] [$\sqrt{x}$]	STAT	**2015.56**
	[$1/x$] [×] [RCL] [=]	STAT	**0.16**
10. Estimate y value for a given x value.			
a. Enter x value (number of hours).	5400	STAT	**5400.00**
b. Compute y value (overhead).	[2nd] [y']	STAT	**26281.97**

Using the results for slope (step 5) and y-intercept (step 4), we have the following equation for the manufacturing overhead:

Overhead Cost = 3.24 (Direct Labor Hours) + 8770.88

The variable overhead rate is $3.24 per hour, and the y-intercept of the line is $8770.88. Since the correlation coefficient (0.99) is a value close to one, you could assume that the equation is a good predictor of the data points within the relevant range of 4000 to 6000 hours. (A coefficient close to zero would indicate that the data does not fit the equation well, which means the equation is not a good predictor.)

The value for the standard error of the regression line, $327.66, means that the actual overhead costs will usually equal the estimated costs ±2 × $327.66. The smaller the standard error is, the more accurate your estimate will be.

The standard error of the slope (.16) indicates that the actual variable overhead rate will usually be equal to $3.24 ± 2 × .16. The smaller this error value is, the more accurate your estimate will be.

For 5400 hours of direct labor, the equation predicts a total overhead amount of $26,281.97. By applying the standard error of the regression line, the actual amount would usually fall within the range of $26,281.97 ± 2 × $327.66 or $25,626.65 to $26,937.25.

NOTE: To obtain valid estimates when you are making predictions with your calculator, the x values entered for any projections must be within the original range of x data points.

*See *Appendix A* for the formulas.

Applying Linear Regression Analysis to Forecasting

Your company has recently started advertising in a series of magazines on a weekly basis. Your marketing manager figures that the advertising campaign of one week will affect the sales volume of the following week, and he has a record of the amount spent on advertising each week (x) and the corresponding sales volume (y). There seems to be a fairly good relationship between the two. What would be the expected sales volume if $1700 is spent on advertising next week? What advertising expense is required to produce $250,000 in sales?

Amount Spent on Advertising (x)	Weekly Sales Volume (y)
$1000	$101,000
$1250	$116,000
$1500	$165,000
$2000	$209,000
$2500	$264,000
$1700	???
???	$250,000

Procedure	Press		Display
1. Clear calculator and mode registers; select two decimal places.	ON/C 2nd CMR FIX 2		**0.00**
2. Select statistical mode ("STAT" shows in the display).	2nd Mode	STAT	**0.00**

Applying Linear Regression Analysis to Forecasting

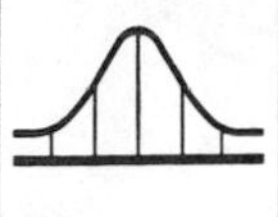

Procedure	Press		Display
3. Enter data. (Calculator displays current number of data entries.)			
a. Enter first x value.	1000 [x:y]	STAT	**0.00**
Enter first y value.	101000 [Σ+]	STAT	**1.00**
b. Enter second pair of data points.	1250 [x:y] 116000 [Σ+]	STAT	**2.00**
c. Enter third pair of data points.	1500 [x:y] 165000 [Σ+]	STAT	**3.00**
d. Enter fourth pair of data points.	2000 [x:y] 209000 [Σ+]	STAT	**4.00**
e. Enter fifth pair of data points.	2500 [x:y] 264000 [Σ+]	STAT	**5.00**
4. Calculate index of determination.	[2nd] [Corr] [x^2]	STAT	**0.99**
5. Calculate y value for x = $1700.	**1700** [2nd] [y']	STAT	**176543.10**
6. Calculate x value for y = $250,000.	**250000** [2nd] [x']	STAT	**2362.60**

Since the index of determination (0.99) is close to one, the regression line is a "good fit" to the data. Based on this straight line approximation, the projected weekly sales volume for $1700 spent on advertising is $176,543.10 and spending $2362.60 on advertising should produce $250,000 in sales.

CHAPTER

11 A Trend Line Analysis

A stock that you've been watching has reported the following earnings per share during the past few years:

$1.52 in 1975
1.35 in 1976
1.53 in 1977
2.17 in 1978
3.60 in 1979

You'd like to predict the earnings per share for the next 3 years. You'd also like to estimate in what year you could expect the earnings per share to reach $6.50.

First, you'll enter your data, using the [x:y] [Σ+] keys. In this case the "x" values are a series of years in sequence, and the "y" values are the stock dividends recorded for each year. (Data for a series of successive years are common for trend line analysis situations.)

Here's an important feature: for trend line analysis your calculator will automatically add 1 to the x variable for you. This means that you can enter the first x value (the first year, 1975) and press [x:y], then enter the y value ($1.52 earnings per share) and press [Σ+]. The first pair of data points is entered. Then you can enter the second data set by just entering the y value (in our case $1.35) and pressing [Σ+]. The calculator automatically increments the x variable for you by one for each entry. This comes in handy when you're analyzing data from successive years.

A Trend Line Analysis

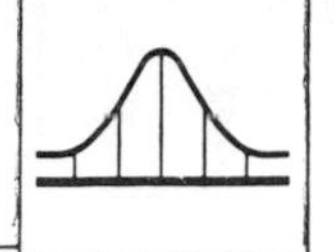

To make predictions on earnings for future years, just enter the year and press [2nd] [x′].

	Procedure	Press		Display
1.	Clear calculator and mode registers; select two decimal places.	[ON/C] [2nd] [CMR] [FIX] 2		0.00
2.	Select statistical mode ("STAT" shows in the display).	[2nd] [Mode]	STAT	0.00
3.	Enter data. (Calculator displays current number of data entries.)	1975 [x:y] 1.52 [Σ+]	STAT	1.00
		1.35 [Σ+]	STAT	2.00
		1.53 [Σ+]	STAT	3.00
		2.17 [Σ+]	STAT	4.00
		3.60 [Σ+]	STAT	5.00
4.	**Predict earnings for 1980, 1981, 1982.**	1980 [2nd] [y′]	STAT	3.53
		1981 [2nd] [y′]	STAT	4.03
		1982 [2nd] [y′]	STAT	4.52
5.	**Predict when earnings should reach $6.50.**	6.50 [2nd] [x′]	STAT	1985.97

Now, see how well the two sets of data are correlated by pressing [2nd] [Corr] and finding 0.85, a fairly good correlation.

CHAPTER

11 Using Learning Curve Analysis

A company has started a new product line and has made the following observations.

Cumulative Units Produced (x)	Average Cumulative Labor Hours Per Unit (y)
50	31
80	24
100	22
125	19.50
160	17.30

Is there a learning curve relationship? If so, what is the learning rate, and how many hours did it take to produce the first unit?

The learning curve ($y=ax^b$) has many applications in modern business, such as scheduling production, projecting unit costs and labor hours, and setting cost and labor standards. More specifically, learning curve analysis can predict whether or not the number of units produced affects the cumulative average time required to produce each unit. If a good relationship exists, the average time needed decreases as the number of units produced increases. Then you can determine the average number of labor hours needed to produce x cumulative units with the equation:

$$y = ax^b$$

where y = average number of labor hours required for production of x cumulative units

a = number of labor hours needed to produce the first unit

x = number of units produced

b = learning rate factor expressed as $\frac{\ln(\text{learning rate})}{\ln(2)}$

The total number of hours required to produce x units is expressed as:

$$yx = ax^{b+1}$$

while the incremental hours required to produce the xth unit are:

$$\text{manhours} = a(b + 1)x^b$$

Using Learning Curve Analysis

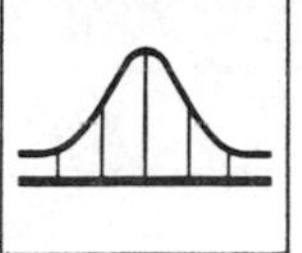

Procedure	Press		Display
1. Clear calculator and mode registers; select two decimal places.	[ON/C] [2nd] [CMR] [FIX] 2		**0.00**
2. Select statistical mode ("STAT" shows in the display).	[2nd] [Mode]	STAT	**0.00**
3. Enter data. (Calculator displays current number of data entries.)			
a. Enter first x value.	50 [2nd] [lnx] [x:y]	STAT	**0.00**
Enter first y value.	31 [2nd] [lnx] [Σ+]	STAT	**1.00**
b. Enter second pair of data points.	80 [2nd] [lnx] [x:y]		
	24 [2nd] [lnx] [Σ+]	STAT	**2.00**
c. Enter third pair of data points.	100 [2nd] [lnx] [x:y]		
	22 [2nd] [lnx] [Σ+]	STAT	**3.00**
d. Enter fourth pair of data points.	125 [2nd] [lnx] [x:y]		
	19.50 [2nd] [lnx] [Σ+]	STAT	**4.00**
e. Enter fifth pair of data points.	160 [2nd] [lnx] [x:y]		
	17.30 [2nd] [lnx] [Σ+]	STAT	**5.00**

(continued on next page)

Procedure	Press		Display
4. Compute correlation between x and y values.	[2nd] [Corr]	STAT	**-1.00**
5. Calculate number of hours required to produce first units.	[2nd] [b/a] [2nd] [e^x]	STAT	**216.17**
6. Calculate learning rate factor (b).	[2nd] [b/a] [x:y]	STAT	**-0.50**
7. Calculate learning rate as a percent.	[×] 2 [2nd] [lnx] [=] [2nd] [e^x] [×] 100 [=]	STAT	**70.81**

The correlation value of −1 indicates that a good negative relationship exists. (As the x values increase, the y values decrease proportionally.) The learning rate is 70.81% and the time needed to produce the first unit is 216.17 hours. The 70.81% rate means that each time you double your lot quantity, the average number of cumulative labor hours is 70.81% times the previous cumulative value. In this example, the average cumulative value was 31 hours per unit for the first 50 units produced. For 100 units (2 × 50), the average cumulative value was 22 hours (31 × 70.81% = 21.95 hours), indicating that 70.81% is a reasonable learning rate estimate. With these values you can go on to calculate your learning curve values, using the procedure in the next example.

Determining the Number of Hours to Produce Units

Your company manufactures a labor intensive product. The time required to produce the first unit was 352.33 hours. Based on past experience, you have an 80% learning curve effect on the average cumulative hours required to complete a unit.

With an 80% learning rate, calculate the following:

(a) average number of hours to produce 100 units
(b) number of hours to produce the 100th unit
(c) total number of hours to produce 100 units

Determining the Number of Hours to Produce Units

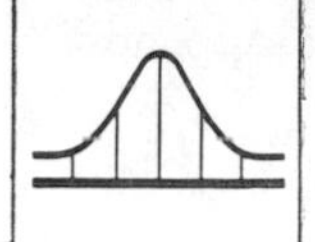

Procedure	Press	Display
1. Clear calculator and select two decimal places.	[ON/C] [STO] [FIX] 2	**0.00**
2. Enter learning rate; calculate and store learning rate factor (b).	80 [%] [2nd] [lnx] [÷] 2 [2nd] [lnx] [=] [STO]	**-0.32**
3. Enter number of units (x) you want to produce and calculate x^b.	100 [2nd] [y^x] [RCL] [=]	**0.23**
4. Multiply by time required to build first unit (a) to calculate average number of hours to produce x (100) units.	[×] 352.33 [=]	**80.00**
5. Calculate hours required to build 100th unit.	[EXC] [+] 1 [×] [RCL] [=]	**54.25**
6. Multiply by number of units to calculate total number of hours needed to produce the first x (100) units.	[RCL] [×] 100 [=]	**8000.06**

With this procedure, you can easily perform a sensitivity analysis to determine the effects on your project from various estimations of your learning rate and the time required to build the first unit, as well as predicting the learning curve values.

Reference:

"The Learning Curve as a Production Tool," Harvard Business Review, pp. 87-97.

Appendix A FORMULAS

Both the formulas used internally by your calculator and the formulas needed to solve specific examples are included here for your information.

FINANCIAL FORMULAS

Definitions of Terms

FV = future value

PV = present value

i = periodic interest rate as a decimal

N = number of compounding periods for compound interest situations or number of payment periods for annuities situations

PMT = periodic payment amount

Compound Interest

When the payment amount is zero, the calculator uses the compound interest equation:

$$FV = PV\,(1 + i)^{N}$$

Annuities

When the payment amount is *not* zero, the calculator uses the annuity equations:

Ordinary Annuity

$$PV = PMT\left[\frac{1 - (1 + i)^{-N}}{i}\right]$$

$$FV = PMT\left[\frac{(1 + i)^{N} - 1}{i}\right]$$

Annuity Due

$$PV = PMT\,(1 + i)\left[\frac{1 - (1 + i)^{-N}}{i}\right]$$

$$FV = PMT\,(1 + i)\left[\frac{(1 + i)^{N} - 1}{i}\right]$$

The interest rate, i, for annuity situations is found through an iterative routine.

Formulas

Principal/Interest

The principal balance for M periods is:

$$BAL\ (M) = PMT \left[\frac{1 - (1 + i)^{-N + M}}{i}\right]$$

The accrued interest for M periods is:

$$ACC\ (M) = M \times PMT + BAL\ (M) - PV$$

The amount of interest in the Mth payment is:

$$I(M) = BAL\ (M - 1) \times i$$

The amount of principal in the Mth payment is:

$$P(M) = PMT - BAL\ (M - 1) \times i$$

INTEREST RATE CONVERSIONS

Compound Interest

Converting a continuous rate to a discrete rate:

$$i = e^{r} - 1$$

Converting a discrete rate to a continuous rate:

$$r = \ln (1 + i)$$

where:

i = equivalent discrete interest rate per compounding period as a decimal

r = continuous interest rate per compounding period as a decimal

Annuities

Converting a continuous rate to a discrete rate:

$$i = e^{r/f} - 1$$

Converting a discrete rate to a continuous rate:

$$r = \ln (1 + i) \times f$$

where:

i = equivalent discrete interest rate per payment period as a decimal

r = annual continuous rate as a decimal

f = number of payments per year

Appendix

Formulas

RULE OF 78's INTEREST AMORTIZATION

total finance charge = N × PMT − loan amount

amount of interest in Kth payment

$$= \frac{N - K + 1}{\text{sum-of-the-years'-digits}} \times \text{total finance charge}$$

where:

$$\text{sum-of-the-years'-digits} = \frac{N(N+1)}{2}$$

unearned interest rebate after K payments

$$= \frac{(N-K)(N-K+1)}{N(N+1)} \times \text{total finance charge}$$

amount of interest paid in K payments = total finance charge − interest rebate

amount required to pay off loan after Kth payment = loan amount + amount of interest paid in K payments − K × PMT

where:

N = total number of payments

PMT = periodic payment amount

K = number of current payment

Reference:

Greynolds, Aronofsky, and Frame, *Financial Analysis Using Calculators: Time Value of Money,* pp. 409 - 413.

PROFIT MARGIN

$$\text{profit margin (\%)} = \frac{\text{sell} - \text{cost}}{\text{sell}} \times 100$$

DEPRECIATION EXPENSE

$$\text{straight-line} = \frac{\text{cost} - \text{salvage}}{N}$$

sum-of-the-years'-digits (SYD) for year N

$$= \frac{\text{cost} - \text{salvage}}{\text{sum-of-the-years'-digits}} \times (N + 1 - \text{year number})$$

where:

$$\text{sum-of-the-years'-digits} = \frac{N\,(N + 1)}{2}$$

$$\text{declining balance} = \text{net book value} \times \frac{\text{declining balance factor}}{N}$$

where depreciation stops when the net book value equals the salvage value.

where:

N = life of asset (number of years)

CAPITAL ASSET PRICING MODEL

The Capital Asset Pricing Model gives the expected rate of return in equilibrium for assumed stock return volatility, risk-free returns, and expected market return. An analyst can use the model to derive the expected future return on a security.

$$E\,(R_i) = R_f + \left[E\,(R_m) - R_f\right] \beta$$

where:

$E\,(R_i)$ = expected future return on the security

R_f = risk-free rate of interest

$E(R_m)$ = expected return on the market portfolio of securities

β = volatility of stock return (degree of responsiveness relative to that of the market portfolio)

Appendix

Formulas

ECONOMIC ORDER QUANTITY

$$EOQ = \left[\frac{2 \times S \times OC}{SC} \right]^{1/2}$$

where:

EOQ = economic order (purchase) quantity

S = annual sales in units

OC = cost per order

SC = cost of carrying one unit in stock for one year

CASH MANAGEMENT MODEL BY MILLER AND ORR

The return point is:

$$Z = \left[\frac{3b\sigma^2}{4i} \right]^{1/3}$$

The upper allowable limit for the cash balance is:

$$h = 3Z$$

where:

Z = point to which the balance is returned

b = cost per transfer between the cash account and the investment account

σ^2 = variance of daily changes in the cash balance

i = daily rate of interest earned on the investment

h = upper allowable limit for the cash balance. Cash in excess of h should be transferred into the investment account.

VALUE OF A GROWTH STOCK

The present value of a stock with a supernormal growth rate, g_S, for N periods and a normal growth rate, g_n, after N periods is the sum of the value of the stock price at the end of the supernormal growth period discounted back to the present and the present value of the dividends paid during the supernormal growth period:

$$\text{Present Value} = \frac{D_o(1 + g_n)}{K_s - g_n}(1 + I)^{-N} + D_o\left[\frac{1 - (1 + I)^{-N}}{I}\right]$$

$$\text{for } I = \frac{1 + K_s}{1 + g_s} - 1$$

where:

D_o = current dividend value

g_n = normal growth rate

K_s = expected rate of return

g_s = supernormal growth rate

N = supernormal growth period

Appendix

Formulas

BONDS

When a bond is purchased between coupon dates with only one coupon payment remaining, daily interest periods are usually assumed. The price (present value) is:

$$PV = 100 \times \left(\left[\frac{\frac{RV}{100} + C_i}{1 + \left(\frac{RD}{TD} \times Y_i\right)} \right] - \left[\frac{AD}{TD} \times C_i \right] \right)$$

where:

PV = present value of the bond on the settlement date per $100 par value

RV = redemption value of the bond per $100 par value

C_i = interest rate per coupon period as a decimal

Y_i = yield per coupon period as a decimal

RD = number of days from the settlement date to the next coupon payment

AD = number of days from the last coupon payment to the settlement date

TD = total number of days in the coupon period

STATISTICS

Definitions of Terms

x = independent variable

y = dependent variable

$\bar{x}$ = mean or average of x values

$\bar{y}$ = mean or average of y values

N = number of elements (or paired x, y elements) in data set

σ_x = standard deviation of x values

σ_y = standard deviation of y values

a = slope of regression line

b = y-intercept of regression line

r = correlation coefficient

Mean, Standard Deviation, and Variance

The mean of the x-values is:

$$\bar{x} = \frac{1}{N} (\Sigma x_i)$$

The mean of the y-values is:

$$\bar{y} = \frac{1}{N} (\Sigma y_i)$$

The standard deviation, with N weighting, of the x-values is:

$$\sigma_x = \left[\frac{\Sigma x^2 - \frac{(\Sigma x)^2}{N}}{N} \right]^{1/2}$$

The standard deviation, with N weighting, of the y-values is:

$$\sigma_y = \left[\frac{\Sigma y^2 - \frac{(\Sigma y)^2}{N}}{N} \right]^{1/2}$$

The standard deviation, with N − 1 weighting, of the x-values is:

$$\sigma_x = \left[\frac{\Sigma x^2 - \frac{(\Sigma x)^2}{N}}{N - 1} \right]^{1/2}$$

The standard deviation, with N−1 weighting, of the y-values is:

$$\sigma_y = \left[\frac{\Sigma y^2 - \frac{(\Sigma y)^2}{N}}{N - 1} \right]^{1/2}$$

The variance of the x-values is $\sigma_x{}^2$.

The variance of the y-values is $\sigma_y{}^2$.

Appendix

Formulas

Linear Regression

$$\text{slope (a)} = \frac{N(\Sigma xy) - (\Sigma y)(\Sigma x)}{N(\Sigma x^2) - (\Sigma x)^2}$$

$$\text{y-intercept (b)} = \frac{\Sigma y - a \Sigma x}{N}$$

$$\text{correlation coefficient} = \frac{a \sigma_x}{\sigma_y}$$

For a given y value, the corresponding x is:

$$x' = (y - \bar{y}) + \bar{x}/a$$

For a given x value, the corresponding y is:

$$y' = a(x - \bar{x}) + \bar{y}$$

The standard error of the regression line is:

$$S_{y/x} = \left[(1 - r^2)\, \sigma_y^2 \times N \times \frac{1}{N - 2} \right]^{1/2}$$

The standard error of the slope is:

$$S_b = \frac{S_{y/x}}{[\sigma_x^2 \times N]^{1/2}}$$

Appendix

B ERROR CONDITIONS

The display shows "Error" when an overflow or underflow occurs, or when an improper operation or key sequence is attempted. When the "Error" condition occurs, no entry from the keyboard (except [OFF]) will be accepted until [ON/C] is pressed. This clears the "Error" condition and any pending calculation. You must now return to the first of your problem and start again or continue from the end of the last valid mode operation if you were doing mode calculations and were interrupted by one of Error Conditions 2 through 11.

You'll get an error message for the following reasons:

1. Calculation resulting in a number outside the range of the calculator (1.0×10^{-99} to 9.9999×10^{99}) in the display, user memory, or mode registers.
2. Dividing a number by zero.
3. Calculating [1/x] or [2nd] [lnx] of zero.
4. Calculating [2nd] [lnx], a power, or a root of a negative number.
5. Calculating [2nd] [Δ%] with x_2 equal to zero.
6. Multiplying a number greater than 1×10^{99} by another number may cause an error condition.
7. Setting up an add-on percent constant with x_1 (first entry) equal to zero.
8. Following the [FIX] key by a key other than the numbers [0] [9] or [ON/C].
9. Following the [DUE] key by a key other than [N], [%i], [PMT], [PV], [FV], [2nd] or [ON/C].
10. Pressing a function key unique to one mode while in another mode. (For example, pressing [%i] when in the statistical mode.)
11. Calculating profit margin with the selling price equal to zero.

The following "Error" conditions will cause the mode registers to be cleared:

12. Attempting to calculate financial unknowns before enough known variables have been entered or when no valid solution exists.

13. Entering statistical data points where the square of a data point, or the sum of the squares of a series of data points, exceeds the upper or lower limit of the calculator.
14. Calculating any statistical function with no data points.
15. Calculating standard deviation (n - 1 weighting) with only one data point.
16. Attempting linear regression calculations with less than two data points.
17. Attempting to calculate the y-intercept/slope or y′ for a vertical line in linear regression.
18. Attempting to calculate x′ for a horizontal line in linear regression.
19. Turning the calculator off while a statistical or financial mode calculation is in progress. The "Error" will appear when the calculator is turned back on.

Clear "Error" condition. In general, pressing ON/C when "Error" is displayed clears the display and any pending arithmetic calculation. If the "Error" condition resulted from a user memory overflow or underflow, the user memory is also cleared. If the "Error" condition resulted from a mode register overflow or underflow, or from a computational error pertaining to the statistical or financial modes (Error conditions 12 through 19 above), the mode registers are cleared. All other Error conditions (2 through 11) which result from illegal key sequences, computation, or data entry can be cleared without affecting the user memory or mode registers.

Appendix

C SERVICE INFORMATION

In Case Of Difficulty

1. If the battery indicator fails to appear on the display, check for improperly inserted or discharged batteries. See Battery Replacement instructions on the following page.
2. If the answer to a calculation seems to be incorrect, press [ON/C], [ON/C], [2nd] [CMR], [FIX] 8, and [STO]. Then repeat the calculation.
3. Review the operating instructions, including the error conditions in *Appendix B,* to be certain that calculations were performed correctly.
4. When batteries are inserted into the calculator and the display does not reset, pressing [OFF] and then [ON/C] should reset the display and prepare the calculator for use.

If none of the above procedures corrects the difficulty, return the calculator PREPAID to the applicable SERVICE FACILITY listed with the warranty.

NOTE: The P.O. box number listed for the Lubbock Service Facility is for United States parcel post shipments only. If you desire to use another carrier, the street address is:

Texas Instruments Incorporated
2305 University Avenue
Lubbock, Texas 79415

For your protection, the calculator should be sent insured; Texas Instruments cannot assume any responsibility for loss or damage during shipment.

Please include information on the difficulty experienced with the calculator, as well as return address information including name, address, city, state and zip code. The shipment should be carefully packaged and adequately protected against shock and rough handling.

Out-of-Warranty Service. *Because our Service Facility serves the entire United States, it is not feasible to hold units while providing repair estimates. For simplicity of operation, we have established flat-rate charges for all out-of-warranty repairs. To obtain the correct charges for a particular model, call our toll-free number listed in this section.*

Battery Replacement

NOTE: Your calculator cannot hold data in its user memory or mode registers if the batteries are removed or become discharged.

Your calculator uses 2 of any of the following batteries: For up to 1000 hours of operation, use Panasonic LR-44 or Ray-O-Vac RW-82. For up to 2500 hours of operation, use Mallory 10L14, Union Carbide (Eveready) 357, Panasonic WL-14, or Toshiba G-13.

1. Turn the calculator off. Remove the carrying case and lay the calculator face down on a soft cloth. Place a small screwdriver, paper clip, or other similar instrument into the slot and gently lift the battery cover.

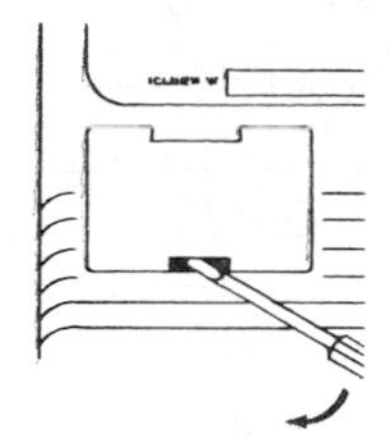

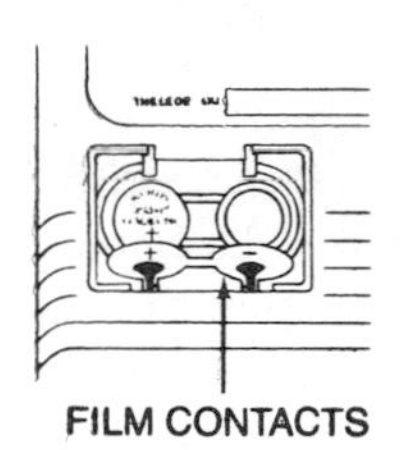

2. Remove the discharged batteries and install new ones as shown. Be careful not to crease the film contacts while installing the new batteries. Be sure the film contacts are positioned to lie on top of the batteries after the batteries are installed.
3. Replace the battery cover top edge first, then gently press until the bottom of the cover snaps into place.
4. Press [ON/C], [ON/C], [2nd] [CMR], [FIX] [8] and [STO] to completely clear the calculator.

Caution: Do not incinerate old batteries.

Calculator Exchange Centers

If your calculator requires service, instead of returning the unit to your dealer or to a service facility for repair, you may elect to exchange the calculator for a factory-reconditioned calculator of the SAME MODEL (or equivalent model specified by TI) by bringing the calculator in person to one of the exchange centers which have been established across the United States. No charge will be made for the exchange with proof-of-purchase during the first 90 days. The exchanged unit will be in warranty for the remainder of the original warranty period or for 6 months, whichever is longer. A HANDLING FEE WILL BE CHARGED FOR EXCHANGE AFTER 90 DAYS FROM THE DATE OF PURCHASE. Out-of-warranty exchanges will be charged at the rates in effect at the time of the exchange.

To determine if there is an exchange center in your locality, look for Texas Instruments Incorporated Exchange Center in the white pages of your telephone directory or look under the Calculator and Adding Machine heading in the yellow pages. Please call the exchange center for availability of your model. Write the Consumer Relations Department for further details and the location of the nearest exchange center.

If You Need Service Information

If you need service information for your calculator, write Consumer Relations at:

Texas Instruments Incorporated
P.O. Box 53
Lubbock, Texas 79408

or call Consumer Relations at 800-858-1802 (toll-free within all contiguous United States except Texas) or 800-692-1353 (toll-free within Texas). If outside the contiguous United States call 806-741-2646. (We regret that we cannot accept collect calls at this number.)

For Technical Assistance

For technical questions relating to specific calculator applications, you can call 806-747-3841. We regret that this is not a toll-free number and we cannot accept collect calls. As an alternative, you can write to the Consumer Relations Department at the address given in the *If You Need Service Information* section.

Service Information

Because of the number of suggestions which come to Texas Instruments from many sources, Texas Instruments will consider such suggestions only if they are freely given to Texas Instruments. It is the policy of Texas Instruments to refuse to receive any suggestions in confidence. Therefore, if you wish to share your suggestions with Texas Instruments or if you wish us to review any calculator applications which you have developed, please include the following in your letter:

> "All of the information forwarded herewith is presented to Texas Instruments on a nonconfidential, nonobligatory basis; no relationship, confidential or otherwise, expressed or implied, is established with Texas Instruments by this presentation. Texas Instruments may use, copyright, distribute, publish, reproduce, or dispose of the information in any way without compensation to me."

Appendix C

ONE-YEAR LIMITED WARRANTY

THIS TEXAS INSTRUMENTS CONSUMER WARRANTY EXTENDS TO THE ORIGINAL CONSUMER PURCHASER OF THE PRODUCT.

WARRANTY DURATION: This Texas Instruments consumer product is warranted to the original consumer purchaser for a period of one year from the original purchase date.

WARRANTY COVERAGE: This Texas Instruments consumer product is warranted against defective materials or workmanship. **THIS WARRANTY DOES NOT COVER THE BATTERIES AND IS VOID IF THE PRODUCT HAS BEEN DAMAGED BY ACCIDENT, UNREASONABLE USE, NEGLECT, IMPROPER SERVICE OR OTHER CAUSES NOT ARISING OUT OF DEFECTS IN MATERIAL OR WORKMANSHIP.**

WARRANTY DISCLAIMERS: ANY IMPLIED WARRANTIES ARISING OUT OF THIS SALE, INCLUDING BUT NOT LIMITED TO THE IMPLIED WARRANTIES OF MERCHANTABILITY AND FITNESS FOR A PARTICULAR PURPOSE, ARE LIMITED IN DURATION TO THE ABOVE ONE YEAR PERIOD. TEXAS INSTRUMENTS SHALL NOT BE LIABLE FOR LOSS OF USE OF THE PRODUCT OR OTHER INCIDENTAL OR CONSEQUENTIAL COSTS, EXPENSES, OR DAMAGES INCURRED BY THE CONSUMER OR ANY OTHER USER.

Some states do not allow the exclusion or limitation of implied warranties or consequential damages, so the above limitations or exclusions may not apply to you in those states.

LEGAL REMEDIES: This warranty gives you specific legal rights, and you may also have other rights that vary from state to state.

WARRANTY PERFORMANCE: During the above one year warranty period, your TI Electronic Calculator will either be repaired or replaced with a reconditioned comparable model (at TI's option) when the Electronic Calculator is returned postage prepaid to a Texas Instruments Service Facility.

The repaired or replacement calculator will continue the warranty of the original unit or six months, whichever is longer. Other than the postage requirement, no charge will be made for such repair or replacement of in-warranty calculators.

TI strongly recommends that you insure the product for value, prior to mailing.

TEXAS INSTRUMENTS CONSUMER SERVICE FACILITIES

U.S. Residents:

Texas Instruments Service Facility
P.O. Box 2500
Lubbock, Texas 79408

Canadian Residents Only:

Geophysical Services Incorporated
41 Shelley Road
Richmond Hill, Ontario, Canada
L4C5G4

Consumers in California and Oregon may contact the following Texas Instruments offices for additional assistance or information.

Texas Instruments Consumer Service
831 South Douglas Street
El Segundo, California 90245
(213) 973-1803

Texas Instruments Consumer Service
6700 Southwest 105th
Kristin Square, Suite 110
Beaverton, Oregon 97005
(503) 643-6758

IMPORTANT NOTICE REGARDING BOOK MATERIALS

TEXAS INSTRUMENTS MAKES NO WARRANTY, EITHER EXPRESSED OR IMPLIED, INCLUDING BUT NOT LIMITED TO ANY IMPLIED WARRANTIES OF MERCHANTABILITY AND FITNESS FOR PARTICULAR PURPOSE, REGARDING THESE BOOK MATERIALS AND MAKES SUCH MATERIALS AVAILABLE SOLELY ON AN "AS-IS" BASIS.

IN NO EVENT SHALL TEXAS INSTRUMENTS BE LIABLE TO ANYONE FOR SPECIAL, COLLATERAL, INCIDENTAL, OR CONSEQUENTIAL DAMAGES IN CONNECTION WITH OR ARISING OUT OF THE PURCHASE OR USE OF THESE BOOK MATERIALS AND THE SOLE AND EXCLUSIVE LIABILITY TO TEXAS INSTRUMENTS, REGARDLESS OF THE FORM OF ACTION, SHALL NOT EXCEED THE PURCHASE PRICE OF THIS BOOK. MOREOVER, TEXAS INSTRUMENTS SHALL NOT BE LIABLE FOR ANY CLAIM OF ANY KIND WHATSOEVER AGAINST THE USER OF THESE BOOK MATERIALS BY ANY OTHER PARTY.

SELECTED BIBLIOGRAPHY

Farish, Roger F.; Greynolds, Elbert B., Jr.; Quiram, Jacquelyn F.; McCollum, Charles L.; and Oliva, Ralph A. *Calculator Analysis for Business and Finance.* Dallas: Texas Instruments, Inc., 1977.

Greynolds, Elbert B., Jr.; Aronofsky, Julius S.; and Frame, Robert J. *Financial Analysis Using Calculators: Time Value of Money.* New York: McGraw-Hill, 1980.

Haney, Jan; Helton, Alecia S.; Stevens, Jan; LaMont, M. Dean; Wilson, C.B.; and Oliva, Ralph A. *Keys to Money Management.* Dallas: Texas Instruments, Inc., 1979.

Hoagland, Henry E.; Stone, Leo D.; and Brueggeman, William B. *Real Estate Finance.* 6th ed. Homewood, IL: Richard D. Irwin, Inc., 1977.

Horngren, Charles T. *Cost Accounting: A Managerial Emphasis.* 4th ed. Englewood Cliffs, NJ: Prentice-Hall, Inc., 1977.

Kieso, Donald E., and Weygandt, Jerry A. *Intermediate Accounting.* 2nd ed. Santa Barbara, CA: John Weily and Sons, 1977.

Kinnard, William N., Jr. *Income Property Valuation.* Lexington, MA: Heath Lexington Books, 1976.

Miller, Merton H., and Orr, Daniel. "A Model of the Demand for Money by Firms." *Quarterly Journal of Economics* 80 (August 1966): 413-435.

Spence, Bruce M.; Graudenz, Jacob Y.; and Lynch, John J. *Standard Securities Calculation Methods.* New York: Securities Industry Association, Inc., 1973.

"The Learning Curve as a Production Tool." *Harvard Business Review,* January-February 1954, pp. 87-97.

Weston, J. Fred, and Brigham, Eugene F. *Managerial Finance.* 6th ed. Hinsdale, IL: The Dryden Press, 1978.

INDEX